THEME SKILLS TESTS
TABLE OF CONTENTS

W9-CFM-536

AUTHOR'S INTRODUCTION

Dear Educator:

Teachers have always used a variety of assessment strategies to help them evaluate student progress and to make instructional decisions. Taken together, these strategies can form a coherent assessment system.

A good assessment system includes three essential elements. First, it includes different types of informal and formal assessments. Second, it helps teachers integrate assessment during instruction and manage the use of classroom portfolios. Finally, both teacher and student self-assessment occur throughout the learning process.

Invitations to Literacy provides teachers with assessment options to fill all these needs. In this program you will find the Integrated Theme Tests, Theme Skills Tests, and Benchmark Progress Tests, as well as the *Teacher's Assessment Handbook.*

Invitations to Literacy also provides extensive support for assessment integrated into the instructional plan in the *Teacher's Book.* There you will find theme Planning for Assessment, opportunities for Informal Assessment and student Self-Assessment, reminders for Portfolio Opportunities, Performance Assessment activities in the Theme Assessment Wrap-Up, and an Informal Assessment Checklist for each theme.

Not all teachers, students, or school districts need the same assessment system. By reviewing the various options in *Invitations to Literacy*, you can determine which pieces best meet your needs. Enjoy the many opportunities assessment provides to get to know your students and to help them grow.

Sheila Valencia

OPTIONS FOR ASSESSMENT IN

Informal Assessment and Self-Assessment

- **Informal Assessment boxes** throughout the *Teacher's Book* signal opportunities to assess children's work during instruction.
- The **Informal Assessment Checklist** helps you record ongoing observations in group or individual formats.
- **Self-Assessment opportunities** appear throughout each theme.
- **Integrated Theme Tests** and **Benchmark Progress Tests** include additional self-assessment opportunities.

Portfolio Assessment

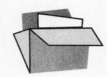

- Many **Portfolio Opportunities** in each theme are identified by Portfolio icons.
- Opportunities include responding, comprehension, writing skills, word skills, communication activities, reading-writing workshops, and performance assessment activities.
- The Portfolio icon appears on *Literacy Activity Book* pages that are especially appropriate for portfolios.
- **Portfolio Assessment notes** in the *Teacher's Book* provide information on these topics: Introducing Portfolios to the Class, Selecting Material for the Portfolio, Grading Work in Portfolios, Conferencing with Children, Evaluating *Literacy Activity Book* Pages, Sending Work Home, Evaluating Oral Language, Peer Conferences, and Using Retellings to Evaluate Comprehension.
- The **Teacher's Assessment Handbook** includes practical teacher tips for organizing, maintaining, and using portfolios.

Managing Assessment

- The **Managing Assessment notes** in the *Teacher's Book* provide practical tips for organizing and managing assessment.
- Topics include Theme Checklists, Testing Options, Work Samples, Report Cards, Making Expectations Clear, Parent Conferences, Monitoring Independent Work, Evaluating Writing, Keeping Anecdotal Notes, Planning Instruction, Setting Personal Goals, and Benchmark Progress Tests.
- Additional topics are included in the *Teacher's Assessment Handbook*.

Performance Assessment

- **Performance Assessment activities** with scoring rubrics appear at the end of each theme in the *Teacher's Book*. Topics include Making an Award; Making Nature Detective Drawings; Making a Web of Friends; Making a Cartoon; Making a Comic Book; Old Story, New Story.
- **Integrated Theme Tests** provide more extended performance assessment options.

Instructional Planning and Placement

• **The Baseline Group Tests** can be given at the beginning of the year to evaluate children's instructional level and to plan the amount of support each child will need.

• The **Informal Reading Inventory** can be administered to individual children to gather additional information about their instructional level and individual instructional needs.

Integrated Theme Tests

• **Apply theme skills** to a new authentic reading selection.

• Provide more extended performance assessment options.

• Can be given at the end of instruction for each theme.

• Have a format that reflects instruction.

• Integrate reading strategies, comprehension, phonics/decoding, writing, and language.

• Include written and multiple-choice answers.

• Can be adapted to meet individual needs.

• Have an easy-to-use Teacher's Edition with rubrics and sample answers at point of use.

• Have been proven in classroom field tests with more than 4,900 children.

Theme Skills Tests

• **Test specific skills** taught in the theme.

• Include comprehension, phonics/decoding, high-frequency words, writing, spelling, grammar, and study skills.

• Can be administered before the theme (pretest) or following the theme.

• Have individual skill subtests that can be administered separately.

• Have a multiple-choice format.

• Are in blackline-master format.

Benchmark Progress Tests

• **Assess children's reading level and writing level** compared to a national sample.

• Measure children's growth in reading and writing over time.

• Can be given at the beginning, middle, and end of the year.

• Have authentic reading selections including narrative and expository text.

• Are independent of program themes—can be scheduled independently.

• Use both written-answer and multiple-choice (multiple correct answer) formats.

• Have an easy-to-use Teacher's Edition with rubrics and sample children's answers at point of use.

• Have been field tested with more than 6,000 children.

• Have results correlated to standardized tests.

FEATURES AT A GLANCE

Theme Skills Tests

✔ Are criterion referenced.

✔ Test specific skills taught in the theme.

✔ Include comprehension, phonics/decoding, high-frequency words, writing, spelling, grammar, and study skills.

✔ Can be administered before the theme (pretest) or following the theme.

✔ Have individual skill subtests that can be administered separately.

✔ Have a multiple-choice format with a single correct answer.

✔ Are in blackline-master format.

USING THE THEME SKILLS TESTS

PURPOSE AND DESCRIPTION

Purpose

The Theme Skills Tests assess children's understanding of discrete reading and language skills taught at each level of *Invitations to Literacy*. The Theme Skills Tests are designed to help you plan instructional support and evaluate children's understanding of these skills. They may also be useful as preparation for certain kinds of standardized assessments.

Description

The Theme Skills Tests are made up of subtests covering comprehension, phonics/decoding, high-frequency words, writing, spelling, grammar, and study skills. The comprehension and phonics/decoding sections are generally divided into a test for each of the individual skills taught in the theme. Each subtest consists of five or ten multiple-choice questions. For each question there is only one correct answer.

- **Comprehension:** Each comprehension subtest includes a passage followed by multiple-choice questions that cover key concepts in the text. The test items evaluate children's ability to comprehend what they have read and to apply the skills to the passage.

- **Phonics/Decoding:** Each subtest is designed to assess children's ability to apply new phonics skills and decoding strategies. Each phonics/decoding skill taught in the theme is tested using

formats such as sentences with blanks to be filled in or questions about underlined words.

- **High-Frequency Words:** Each item in this subtest consists of vocabulary-controlled sentences containing a blank, followed by word choices. This section provides the opportunity for children to give evidence of their ability to recognize the high-frequency words introduced in the theme.

- **Writing:** Five questions in the writing subtest assess children's understanding of the writing skills taught in the theme.

- **Spelling:** The spelling subtest assesses children's ability to recognize the correct spelling of words they have studied in the theme. Children read several sentences, each containing a blank. They must choose the answer that is spelled correctly.

- **Grammar:** The grammar subtest consists of five items. It checks children's understanding of the grammar skills taught in the theme.

- **Study Skills:** This subtest is designed to assess children's ability to apply one of the study skills taught in the theme, such as parts of a book, reading a map, or using an encyclopedia. (Note: At Level 2, not all Theme Skills Tests contain a tested Study Skill.)

ADMINISTERING THE THEME SKILLS TESTS

You can schedule the use of the tests in any of several ways:

- After completing a theme, you can administer the entire Theme Skills Test or selected subtests to help determine how well children understand the theme skills.

- You can administer selected subtests at the beginning of a theme. The results of the test can help you plan the amount of instructional support you need to provide.

- You can administer any parts of the test during the course of the year in order to evaluate areas where children may need additional help.

When you administer one or more parts of the tests, you may want to follow these guidelines:

- Copy and distribute the test or subtests to be given. Make sure children are completing the correct portions of the test.

- Check to make sure children understand how to take the test and how to mark their answers. You may wish to administer or review the Practice Test. For the Practice Test, read the directions with children and have them complete the test. Then discuss the correct answers with them.

- At the beginning of each subtest, read the directions together. Then allow children to work independently, but help them with any directions they do not understand.

- Allow children sufficient time to complete the subtests, using as many sessions as you feel are necessary.

SCORING

Using the Theme Skills Test Record Form

Because the Theme Skills Test is a simple multiple-choice evaluation, scoring is direct and objective. Correct answers are shown on the annotated pages of the Teacher's Edition. In general, a score of 80 percent on any section of the test should be accepted as an indication of satisfactory performance.

Providing Additional Support

If a child answers fewer than four out of five questions correctly, he or she may need more help with the particular skill. It is important, however, to consider other evidence of a child's growth in reading (from other assessment instruments and your own observations) before concluding that the child is not performing satisfactorily. For example, you may want to review your notes on the Informal Assessment Checklist or the child's work on *Literacy Activity Book* pages for the skill.

If other information suggests that the student is having difficulty with the skill, you may want to consider these options:

- Monitor the student's work on similar skills in the next theme's instruction for an overall view of his or her progress. Check the Skill Finder in Part 3, Instruct and Integrate, for the next occurrence of the skill in the level. You may wish to give special attention to the student in teaching this next lesson.

- Check the Skill Finder in Part 3, Instruct and Integrate, for Minilessons on the skill within the theme and earlier in the level. If you have not used these Minilessons, you may wish to consider using them in a small group or with the individual student to provide extra support for the skill.

- You may wish to use *Literacy Activity Book* pages for the skill as material for an additional minilesson with the individual student, or with a small group of students who need additional support.

PRACTICE TEST

Read the selection. Then read each question. Fill in the circle next to the best answer.

How can people get to faraway places? One way is by air. Every day jet planes take people to many great places. Jet planes are very fast, and they can take many people at the same time. These planes take off and land at places called airports.

1. What are all the sentences about?

- ○ a. why people go away
- ● b. going by jet plane
- ○ c. cars
- ○ d. airports

2. Which word tells about jets?

- ○ a. little
- ○ b. quiet
- ● c. fast
- ○ d. slow

PET SHOW TODAY!
LEVEL 2, THEME 1
Theme Skills Test Record

Student _____ Date _____

STUDENT RECORD FORM	Possible Score	Criterion Score	Student Score
Part A: Story Structure and Summarizing	5	4	
Part B: Inferences: Drawing Conclusions	5	4	
Part C: Fantasy and Realism	5	4	
Part D: Consonant Clusters: *gl, gr, sn, sp, st*	5	4	
Part E: Consonant Digraphs: *sh, ch, ck*	5	4	
Part F: Consonant Digraphs: *th, wh*	5	4	
Part G: High-Frequency Words	5	4	
Part H: Writing	5	4	
Part I: Spelling	10	8	
Part J: Grammar	5	4	
Part K: Study Skills	5	4	
TOTAL	60	48	
Total Student Score x 1.67 =			%

STORY STRUCTURE AND SUMMARIZING

Read this story. Then read each question and fill in the circle next to your answer.

Pet Problems

Darren was playing at Kim's house. They made a house from boxes. But Kim's puppy tipped the boxes over.

"No, Chip!" Darren said.

Then Kim and Darren made another house. They put a sheet over two chairs. The puppy pulled down the sheet with his teeth.

"No, Chip!" said Kim.

"What can we do?" asked Darren. "Chip keeps messing up our houses."

Go on

Kim thought about it. "We can draw houses on this art paper," she said.

When Darren and Kim were done drawing their houses, they drew a doghouse for Chip. "Now we each have a house, and Chip can't mess them up!" said Kim.

1. Where does this story take place?

   ○ a. on a farm
   ○ b. at the zoo
   ○ c. at Darren's house
   ● d. at Kim's house

2. Who is this story mostly about?

   ● a. Kim and Darren
   ○ b. Chip and Darren
   ○ c. Chip and Kim
   ○ d. Kim and her family

3. What are Darren and Kim trying to do in this story?

   ● a. They are making houses.
   ○ b. They are running a race.
   ○ c. They are swimming.
   ○ d. They are eating.

4. What problem do Darren and Kim have?

    ○ a. They have to help Darren's sister.

    ○ b. Chip has nowhere to live.

    ● c. Chip messes up what they build.

    ○ d. Kim's mother says it's time to stop.

5. How do they solve the problem?

    ○ a. Darren goes home.

    ● b. Kim and Darren draw houses on art paper.

    ○ c. Kim and Darren make a tree house.

    ○ d. Kim starts to cry.

Stop

INFERENCES: DRAWING CONCLUSIONS

Read this story. Then read each question and fill in the circle next to the best answer.

The Pet Trick

Carlos was sad. He wanted a pet, but pet fur made him sneeze. Dad said he would help Carlos find a good pet.

They went to the pet store. "May I help you?" asked a man working in the store.

"I need a pet that doesn't have fur," said Carlos.

"I can help you," said the man. "Other kinds of pets are fun, too."

The man showed Carlos and Dad many pets. They saw fish, snakes, and toads. "Can they do tricks?" asked Carlos.

"Not really," said the man. He saw Carlos frown.

"I know what you'd like!" said the man. He showed Carlos a bowl.

"Those are funny fish!" said Carlos.

Go on

"These pets do a great trick," said the man. "Soon they will turn into frogs."

Carlos smiled. "What a trick!" he said. "Dad, may I have one?"

"Sure!" said Dad.

1. Why did the man show Carlos fish, snakes, and toads?

   ● a. They don't have fur.
   ○ b. They move slowly.
   ○ c. They can live in a house.
   ○ d. The man liked those pets.

2. Why did Carlos frown about the fish, snakes, and toads?

   ○ a. They were too big.
   ● b. They didn't do tricks.
   ○ c. Dad said he couldn't have them.
   ○ d. They had fur.

3. How does Carlos feel about frogs?

   ○ a. They make him sad.
   ○ b. He is afraid of them.
   ● c. He likes them.
   ○ d. He doesn't like them.

Go on

4. Which of these pets would make Carlos sneeze?

- ○ a. a frog
- ○ b. a snake
- ○ c. a toad
- ● d. a cat

5. Which of these sentences do you think Carlos might say?

- ○ a. "Fish have too much fur."
- ○ b. "Dad doesn't like pets."
- ○ c. "A frog is no fun."
- ● d. "This is a great pet for me!"

Draw a picture to show what the pet will look like when it grows up. *(No score for this item.)*

C FANTASY AND REALISM

Read each story. Then read the questions that follow. Fill in the circle next to the best answer.

"Look at that," said Nip the cat as she licked her paws. "My kite is up in the tree."

"I'll get it," said Jasper. Jasper was Nip's friend. He was a big, brown dog. "Just let me chew on this bone for a bit. Then I'll fly to the top of the tree and get your kite down."

Soon Jasper handed the kite to Nip. "Thanks, Jasper," said Nip. "You are a good friend."

"Now let's fly that kite together," said Jasper.

1. Which of these things could **not** really happen?

   - ● a. a cat flying a kite
   - ○ b. a cat licking its paws
   - ○ c. a cat drinking water
   - ○ d. a cat sleeping

2. Which of these things **can** a dog really do?

   - ○ a. talk to a cat
   - ○ b. fly to the top of a tree
   - ● c. chew on a bone
   - ○ d. fly a kite

Go on ⟹

3. How did you know this story was a fantasy?

○● a. Dogs and cats can't really talk or fly.
○ b. Dogs and cats like to fly kites.
○ c. Dogs and cats live on farms.
○ d. Dogs don't chew bones.

Ana got a pet mouse. She put the mouse in a cage. "I will take good care of you," said Ana. "I'll give you food and water each day. I'll clean your cage too. I must also give you a name."

Ana could not think of a good name for her pet. She watched what her mouse did. He let her pick him up. He hid in a tube in his cage. He ate nuts. Ana knew that nuts were good for her pet. Hard food would keep his front teeth from growing too long.

"Nutty!" said Ana. "That's a great name for you."

"My name is Harry," said the mouse. "But you can call me Nutty if you want to. I do like nuts. May I please have some now?"

4. Which one is something a real mouse could **not** do?

- ○ a. hide in a tube
- ○ b. eat nuts
- ○ c. live in a cage
- ● d. tell someone its name

5. How did you know this story was a fantasy?

- ○ a. Ana picked up her pet.
- ● b. The mouse talked.
- ○ c. The mouse grew long teeth.
- ○ d. Ana talked to her pet.

Stop

CONSONANT CLUSTERS *(gl, gr, sn, sp, st)*

Read the following sentences and think about what word might go in the blank. Then fill in the circle next to the best answer.

1. "Look at my new pet, Mom," said Sami. "It has a shell. My pet is a _____ ."

   ○ a. smile
   ○ b. dress
   ○ c. sail
   ● d. snail

2. "That's a funny pet," said Mom. "I don't know if it should _____ inside."

   ● a. stay
   ○ b. street
   ○ c. say
   ○ d. sky

3. "Please, Mom," Sami said. "He has dots on his shell, so I can name him _____ ."

   ○ a. Snip
   ○ b. Swim
   ○ c. Step
   ● d. Spot

4. "Your pet can't live in our house, Sami. His shell is his house. I think your pet would be happier in the _____ ."

- ○ a. gas
- ● b. grass
- ○ c. glass
- ○ d. class

5. "You're right, Mom," said Sami. "I'll let him go. He'll be _____ I did."

- ○ a. gray
- ● b. glad
- ○ c. gate
- ○ d. clay

Stop

E

CONSONANT DIGRAPHS: sh, ch, ck

Read each sentence and think about what word might go in the blank. Fill in the circle next to the best answer.

1. "I'd like to have a pet," said Chris. "That would be fun. The kind of pet I want won't _____ cars."

   ○ a. case
   ● b. chase
   ○ c. clash
   ○ d. inch

2. "A pet needs care _____ day," said Grandpa. "Would you feed it? Would you clean up after it? Would you give it a bath?"

   ● a. each
   ○ b. cheap
   ○ c. beak
   ○ d. leash

3. "I would feed it, Grandpa," said Chris. "I would clean its home. But you don't have to _____ the kind of pet I want."

○ a. chin
○ b. was
● c. wash
○ d. shawl

4. "Well then, you must want a _____ ," said Grandpa.

○ a. shin
● b. fish
○ c. fleck
○ d. shape

5. "Let's go down to the pet shop and you can _____ one out," said Grandpa.

○ a. patch
○ b. polish
○ c. chick
● d. pick

Stop

F CONSONANT DIGRAPHS: th, wh

Read each sentence and think about what word might go in the blank. Then fill in the circle next to the best answer.

1. I wanted to _____ my uncle for Benny, the puppy he gave me.
   - ○ a. tank
   - ○ b. other
   - ○ c. with
   - ● d. thank

2. "I _____ Uncle Rolando would like to see you," I told Benny.
   - ○ a. both
   - ● b. think
   - ○ c. trick
   - ○ d. time

3. "_____ will you be back?" asked Mother.
   - ○ a. Hen
   - ○ b. Chop
   - ● c. When
   - ○ d. Thin

Go on

4. "When we get _____ , I'll call you and let you know," I told her.

- ○ a. bath
- ● b. there
- ○ c. tall
- ○ d. which

5. Benny was so happy to see Uncle Rolando that he didn't know _____ to do.

- ○ a. both
- ○ b. that
- ● c. what
- ○ d. how

G HIGH-FREQUENCY WORDS

Read the following sentences and think about what word might go in the blank. Then fill in the circle next to the best answer.

1. "My _____ is going on a trip," said Janelle. "Will you feed our cat?"

    ○ a. street
    ○ b. friends
    ● c. family
    ○ d. hour

2. "I'll be glad to," said Mr. Johnson. "I will take good _____ of her."

    ● a. care
    ○ b. watch
    ○ c. pick
    ○ d. better

3. "Thank you, Mr. Johnson," said Janelle. "I feel _____ knowing that she'll be with you."

    ○ a. quietly
    ● b. better
    ○ c. these
    ○ d. left

4. "Why don't you bring her by in an _____ ,"
said Mr. Johnson.

○ a. said
○ b. night
○ c. far
● d. hour

5. Janelle went home and _____ her cat,
"You're going to visit a friend!"

● a. told
○ b. family
○ c. stay
○ d. care

Stop

H WRITING *(writing complete sentences)*

Find each complete sentence. Fill in the circle next to the best answer.

1. ◯ a. Lucy and a pet snake.
 ◯ b. Had a pet snake.
 ● c. Lucy had a pet snake.
 ◯ d. Lucy's pet snake.

2. ● a. The snake was in a cage.
 ◯ b. In a cage.
 ◯ c. The snake.
 ◯ d. Was in a cage.

3. ◯ a. The snake out.
 ◯ b. One day out.
 ● c. One day the snake got out.
 ◯ d. One day the snake.

Go on

4.
- ○ a. Lucy and her mother.
- ○ b. Under the bed.
- ○ c. Looked under the bed.
- ● d. Lucy and her mother looked under the bed.

5.
- ○ a. Found the snake.
- ● b. They found the snake.
- ○ c. Lucy and her mother.
- ○ d. The snake and Lucy and her mother.

Stop

SPELLING

Read the sentence with the missing word. Then find the correct way to spell the word, and fill in the circle next to your answer.

1. I _____ saw my friend Teresa. *(consonant clusters)*

    ○ a. jast

    ● b. just

    ○ c. juhst

    ○ d. jost

2. She has a new _____ mouse named Bianca. *(words with* th *or* wh*)*

    ○ a. whit

    ○ b. whyte

    ● c. white

    ○ d. whyt

3. Bianca is so _____ fun! *(words with* sh *or* ch*)*

    ● a. much

    ○ b. mich

    ○ c. mach

    ○ d. mush

4. We played _____ her all day. *(words with th or wh)*

- ○ a. whith
- ○ b. wyth
- ○ c. wiwh
- ● d. with

5. I liked it _____ she climbed up my arm. *(words with th or wh)*

- ○ a. wen
- ● b. when
- ○ c. whin
- ○ d. wyn

6. After lunch Bianca fell asleep in her food

_____ · *(words with sh or ch)*

- ● a. dish
- ○ b. dich
- ○ c. dysh
- ○ d. dych

7. We thought _____ was very funny. *(words with th or wh)*

- ○ a. thate
- ○ b. tat
- ● c. that
- ○ d. phat

Go on ⟹

8. Now I _____ I had my own mouse. *(words with sh or ch)*

   ● a. wish
   ○ b. wich
   ○ c. wysh
   ○ d. whish

9. I'm _____ I got to see Teresa and Bianca. *(consonant clusters)*

   ○ a. glay
   ○ b. stad
   ● c. glad
   ○ d. chad

10. It's fun to _____ at Teresa's house! *(consonant clusters)*

   ○ a. stae
   ○ b. sey
   ○ c. scay
   ● d. stay

GRAMMAR *(naming parts and action parts)*

Read each sentence. Then read each question and fill in the circle next to the best answer.

1. Angie has a goat called Star.

   Which is the naming part of that sentence?
   - ● a. Angie
   - ○ b. has
   - ○ c. called
   - ○ d. has a goat called Star

2. Star runs fast.

   Which is the action part of that sentence?
   - ○ a. Star
   - ● b. runs fast
   - ○ c. Star runs fast
   - ○ d. fast

3. Dad helps Angie with Star.

   Which is the naming part of that sentence?
   - ● a. Dad
   - ○ b. helps
   - ○ c. with
   - ○ d. helps Angie with Star

Go on ⇒

4. Angie and Star go to the state fair.

Which is the action part of that sentence?

- ○ a. the state fair
- ○ b. Angie and Star go to the state fair
- ○ c. Angie and Star
- ● d. go to the state fair

5. The goat wins many prizes.

Which is the naming part of that sentence?

- ● a. The goat
- ○ b. wins many prizes
- ○ c. The goat wins many prizes
- ○ d. many

STUDY SKILLS *(parts of a book)*

Study the table of contents. Then read each question. Fill in the circle next to the best answer.

Table of Contents

Chapter 1 Picking a Dog 2

Chapter 2 Feeding Your Dog 5

Chapter 3 Training Your Dog 9

Chapter 4 What to Do If Your Dog
Gets Sick 13

1. On which page does Chapter 3 begin?

○ a. 5

○ b. 2

● c. 9

○ d. 13

2. Which chapter would you read to find out what to feed your dog?

○ a. Chapter 1

● b. Chapter 2

○ c. Chapter 3

○ d. Chapter 4

3. On which page would you begin reading to learn how to pick out a good dog?

- ○ a. 13
- ○ b. 5
- ○ c. 9
- ● d. 2

4. On which page does Chapter 4 begin?

- ● a. 13
- ○ b. 9
- ○ c. 2
- ○ d. 5

5. Which chapter would you read to find out what to do for a sick dog?

- ○ a. Picking a Dog
- ○ b. Training Your Dog
- ● c. What to Do If Your Dog Gets Sick
- ○ d. Feeding Your Dog

BE A NATURE DETECTIVE

LEVEL 2, THEME 2

Theme Skills Test Record

Student _____ Date _____

STUDENT RECORD FORM			
	Possible Score	Criterion Score	Student Score
Part A: Text Organization and Summarizing	5	4	
Part B: Compare and Contrast	5	4	
Part C: Categorize and Classify	5	4	
Part D: Noting Details	5	4	
Part E: Short Vowels: *a, i, u* (CVC)	5	4	
Part F: Short Vowels: *e, o* (CVC)	5	4	
Part G: Long Vowels: CVCe	5	4	
Part H: Compound Words **Words with *nd, ng, nk***	5	4	
Part I: High-Frequency Words	5	4	
Part J: Writing	5	4	
Part K: Spelling	10	8	
Part L: Grammar	5	4	
Part M: Study Skills	5	4	
TOTAL	70	56	
Total Student Score x 1.43 =			%

A TEXT ORGANIZATION AND SUMMARIZING

Read this selection. Then read each question and fill in the circle next to the best answer.

Animal Watching

Watching animals can be fun for you. Make it fun for the animals, too. When you go to watch animals, move slowly and quietly. Stay back. The animals won't like it if you get too close.

If you want to see the animals fly or run, just wait. Don't run after them. An animal could harm itself or harm you by trying to get away.

When you leave, say thanks. Isn't that what you say when you've been to see other friends? So be a friend to animals!

Go on →

1. What is the selection mostly about?

   ○ a. how to buy a dog
   ○ b. saying thanks to animals
   ● c. what to do when watching animals
   ○ d. making animals fly or run

2. What is one important idea from the selection about watching animals?

   ● a. Don't chase animals.
   ○ b. Some animals run.
   ○ c. You say thanks after you visit your friends.
   ○ d. Some animals fly.

3. What detail tells you how you should **move** when you watch animals?

   ○ a. Say thanks.
   ○ b. The animals won't like it if you get too close.
   ○ c. Watching animals can be fun for you.
   ● d. You should move slowly and quietly.

Go on ⟹

4. Why shouldn't you chase animals?

- ○ a. An animal doesn't need to fly or run.
- ○ b. An animal likes to play games.
- ● c. An animal could harm itself or you by trying to get away.
- ○ d. An animal might get lost if it flies or runs away.

5. Which of these is **not** a main idea from the selection?

- ● a. Take animals home with you.
- ○ b. When watching animals, stay back.
- ○ c. Don't chase the animals.
- ○ d. Say thanks to the animals.

Stop

B COMPARE AND CONTRAST

Read this selection. Then read each question and fill in the circle next to the best answer.

Many Kinds of Nests

Many animals build nests. If you look around, you might see some of them.

Have you ever seen an ant nest? You can't see most of the nest. It can be under the ground or inside a log. An ant nest has many rooms. Many ant nests are very big. Sometimes they are bigger than a bathtub!

A crow makes a big nest, too. The nest is made mostly of sticks and grasses. Crows make their nests in big trees.

A black duck makes a nest right on the ground near some water. It is made with grasses, and the mother duck puts some of her own down inside the nest. The nest is about as big as a cowboy hat.

Next time you are outdoors, see what kinds of nests you can find. It is fun to see how animals build nests!

1. Which is true about **all** the nests in the selection?

   ○ a. They are all made of sticks.
   ○ b. They are all under the ground.
   ● c. They are all made by animals.
   ○ d. They are all small.

2. How is an ant's nest **not** like a crow's or a duck's nest?

   ○ a. It is a home for animals.
   ○ b. It is made by animals.
   ○ c. It is fun to look at.
   ● d. It can be under the ground.

3. What does an ant's nest have that a crow's nest does **not** have?

   ● a. many rooms
   ○ b. duck down
   ○ c. eggs
   ○ d. sticks and grasses

4. Which of these sentences is true?

- ○ a. A duck's nest is bigger than a bathtub.
- ● b. A duck's nest is smaller than a bathtub.
- ○ c. A crow's nest is very small.
- ○ d. All ants' nests are tiny.

5. How is a duck's nest **like** a crow's nest?

- ○ a. They are both under the ground.
- ● b. They are both made with grasses.
- ○ c. They are both bigger than a bathtub.
- ○ d. They are both made of clay.

C

CATEGORIZE AND CLASSIFY

Read this story. Then read each question and fill in the circle next to the best answer.

Where Do You Watch Animals?

Tony and Anita were talking about animals they like to watch. "I like to go to the seashore and watch snails and crabs," said Tony. "Their shells are so pretty."

"You're right," said Anita. "Fish and frogs are fun to watch, too. Fish swim so fast, and I love the way frogs jump!"

"Where do you like to watch animals?" asked Tony.

"I like to go to my uncle's farm," said Anita. "I can look for little mice there. Sometimes I see flying bats. There are also crows at the farm. They fly all over the place."

"Are there any goats or deer there?" asked Tony. "They look so funny when they run and jump."

"Yes. It's a great place to watch animals," said Anita.

Go on ⟹

1. Which of the animals you read about have shells?

   ○ a. goats and deer
   ● b. snails and crabs
   ○ c. bats and mice
   ○ d. fish and frogs

2. Which group of animals can **all** live in the water?

   ○ a. bats, mice, and crows
   ○ b. snails, mice, and deer
   ○ c. mice, crows, and fish
   ● d. frogs, fish, and crabs

3. In which group do bats and crows belong?

   ○ a. animals that swim
   ○ b. animals with fur
   ● c. animals with wings
   ○ d. animals with shells

Go on ⇒

4. Which of these animals can run and jump?

- ○ a. snails
- ○ b. bats
- ● c. deer
- ○ d. fish

5. Which of these animals has feathers?

- ● a. crow
- ○ b. fish
- ○ c. fox
- ○ d. snail

D NOTING DETAILS

Read this story. Then read each question and fill in the circle next to the best answer.

Grandma, the Nature Spy

Darnell and Grandma were going for a walk in the woods. Darnell knew he would have fun with Grandma. He thought they would see birds. He thought they might even see some other animals. What he didn't know was that Grandma would become a nature spy!

Right away, Grandma showed him something new. "Look at this plant, Darnell," said Grandma. She turned over a leaf. Darnell saw many little eggs there. "These will be bugs!" Grandma said with a smile.

They walked by a stream. "Do you see where the grass is flat?" asked Grandma. "Deer may have rested there."

"Now be very quiet," Grandma said. Then she stopped by a tall tree. "Can you hear it?" she asked. "It sounds like baby birds. There may be a nest."

They looked up at the top of the tree. There was the nest! Grandma was right.

Then it was time to go. Darnell smiled. Next time, he would be a nature spy too.

1. Where did Grandma find bugs' eggs?

- ○ a. in a cup
- ○ b. in the top of a tree
- ● c. on a leaf
- ○ d. on Darnell's clothes

2. Why did Grandma think deer might have been near the stream?

- ● a. The grass was flat.
- ○ b. The sun was out.
- ○ c. She saw deer running away.
- ○ d. She likes deer.

3. Why did Grandma think a bird's nest might be near?

- ○ a. There was a stream in the woods.
- ○ b. The grass by the stream was flat.
- ○ c. She saw fox tracks in the sand.
- ● d. There were sounds from baby birds.

Go on

4. What are some things from the story that tell you Darnell and Grandma were in the woods?

- ● a. They saw plants, trees, and a stream.
- ○ b. They saw a barn, a cow, and a house.
- ○ c. They saw a building, a bus, and a sidewalk.
- ○ d. They saw swings, a slide, and a seesaw.

5. What surprised Darnell about the walk in the woods?

- ○ a. They saw birds and other animals.
- ● b. Grandma became a nature spy.
- ○ c. There were trees and a stream.
- ○ d. Grandma said it was time to go home.

E

SHORT VOWELS: a, i, u (CVC)

Read this selection. Look at the underlined words. Then read each question and fill in the circle next to the best answer.

What animal likes water but is not a <u>fish</u>? What animal can't run but can <u>jump</u>? It's a frog!

Frogs use their strong <u>back</u> legs to jump. By jumping, they can get away <u>fast</u>. If you try to <u>pick</u> up a frog, it will jump. Have fun with frogs just by looking at them.

1. Which word has the same vowel sound you hear in the word **fish**?

- ● a. win
- ○ b. fine
- ○ c. night
- ○ d. date

2. Which word has the same vowel sound you hear in the word **jump**?

- ○ a. cube
- ○ b. dot
- ● c. puppy
- ○ d. jam

Go on ⇨

3. Which word has the same vowel sound you hear in the word **back**?

- ○ a. bake
- ○ b. been
- ○ c. brave
- ● d. pad

4. Which word has the same vowel sound you hear in the word **fast**?

- ○ a. sick
- ○ b. fake
- ○ c. dust
- ● d. pass

5. Which word has the same vowel sound you hear in the word **pick**?

- ● a. thin
- ○ b. pine
- ○ c. run
- ○ d. time

F

SHORT VOWELS: e, o (CVC)

Read this selection. Look at the underlined words. Then read each question and fill in the circle next to the best answer.

When baby birds are a few weeks old, many leave the <u>nest</u>. The mother bird will <u>send</u> them out to find food. The baby birds fly in the air. They also <u>hop</u> along the ground. Then the baby birds <u>rest</u>.

The birds might take a long trip. Sometimes a <u>flock</u> of birds goes far away for the winter.

1. Which word has the same vowel sound you hear in the word **nest**?

   ○ a. need
   ○ b. mean
   ● c. left
   ○ d. me

2. Which word has the same vowel sound you hear in the word **send**?

   ○ a. see
   ○ b. sea
   ○ c. Pete
   ● d. net

Go on ⇒

3. Which word has the same vowel sound you hear in the word **hop**?

  ● a. not
  ○ b. hook
  ○ c. coat
  ○ d. joke

4. Which word has the same vowel sound you hear in the word **rest**?

  ○ a. ride
  ● b. bed
  ○ c. weed
  ○ d. she

5. Which word has the same vowel sound you hear in the word **flock**?

  ● a. stop
  ○ b. foot
  ○ c. load
  ○ d. woke

G LONG VOWELS: CVCe

**Read the story. Look at the underlined words.
Then read each question and fill in the circle next
to your answer.**

"<u>Wake</u> up, Luke," said Jake. "It's time to <u>hike</u>."

"Is this a <u>joke</u>?" asked Luke. "The sun isn't up!"

Then Jake sang a little <u>tune</u>. "Up with the sun,
and you'll have fun. See what you can see! A bird
flies in the sky. Another animal runs by. Come and
hike with me."

"I'm up," said Luke. "Let's <u>race</u> to the woods."

1. Which word has the same vowel sound you hear
   in the word **wake**?

   ○ a. mad
   ● b. made
   ○ c. dive
   ○ d. wet

2. Which word has the same vowel sound you hear
   in the word **hike**?

   ● a. bite
   ○ b. hat
   ○ c. sea
   ○ d. hit

Go on

3. Which word has the same vowel sound you hear in the word **joke**?

- ○ a. not
- ○ b. book
- ○ c. soon
- ● d. note

4. Which word has the same vowel sound you hear in the word **tune**?

- ● a. cute
- ○ b. up
- ○ c. tip
- ○ d. time

5. Which word has the same vowel sound you hear in the word **race**?

- ○ a. ripe
- ○ b. cube
- ● c. take
- ○ d. flat

COMPOUND WORDS
WORDS WITH nd, ng, nk

Read the sentences and think about what word might go in each blank. Then fill in the circle next to the best answer.

1. The _____ is a good place to look at fish.

   ○ a. toothbrush
   ○ b. afternoon
   ● c. seashore
   ○ d. seashell

2. One kind of fish is named after a tool. It is called a _____ .

   ● a. sawfish
   ○ b. airport
   ○ c. bedtime
   ○ d. doorbell

3. A sawfish can be up to twenty feet _____ .

   ○ a. wing
   ● b. long
   ○ c. ring
   ○ d. link

Go on ⇨

4. I saw one once. It was in a big _____ .

- ○ a. wink
- ● b. think
- ● c. tank
- ○ d. sing

5. If I were a sawfish, I would use my saw to dig in the _____ .

- ○ a. band
- ○ b. pink
- ○ c. sank
- ● d. sand

HIGH-FREQUENCY WORDS

Read the sentences and think about what word might go in each blank. Then fill in the circle next to the best answer.

1. The time to see bats is at night. That is when a bat _____ its hunting.

   ○ a. sea
   ○ b. car
   ● c. does
   ○ d. wish

2. A bat's _____ can't see much, but a bat can hear from very far away.

   ○ a. open
   ○ b. been
   ○ c. another
   ● d. eye

3. Bats help plants _____ . Just like bees, they take flower dust from plant to plant.

   ● a. grow
   ○ b. does
   ○ c. jump
   ○ d. brown

Go on ⇨

4. A bat can fly very fast as it _____ from one plant to another.

- ○ a. bird
- ● b. goes
- ○ c. size
- ○ d. green

5. A bat is one _____ that can be found in many places.

- ○ a. lead
- ○ b. island
- ● c. animal
- ○ d. end

WRITING

Read the paragraph. Then read each question and fill in the circle next to the best answer.

Ponds are places where many animals live. You might have seen some animals in a pond. Did you know that many animals that are too tiny for you to see also live there? They make their home in the water. Don't drink pond water! It is someone's home.

1. Which sentence tells what the paragraph is mostly about? *(writing a paragraph)*

- ○ a. It is fun to go to a pond.
- ● b. Ponds are places where many animals live.
- ○ c. Don't drink pond water!
- ○ d. Ducks live on farms.

2. Which sentence **asks** something? *(kinds of sentences)*

- ● a. Did you know that tiny animals live in ponds?
- ○ b. Don't drink pond water!
- ○ c. Many animals live in ponds.
- ○ d. A pond is someone's home.

3. Which sentence is an **exclamation**? *(kinds of sentences)*

○ a. Did you know that many animals that are too tiny for you to see also live there?

○ b. Ponds are places where many animals live.

○ c. They make their home in the water.

● d. Don't drink pond water!

4. How many telling sentences are there in the paragraph? *(kinds of sentences)*

● a. four

○ b. one

○ c. six

○ d. two

5. Which sentence tells the most? *(writing clearly with nouns)*

○ a. Animals live in water.

○ b. Animals live in ponds.

○ c. Fish, ducks, and frogs live in water.

● d. Fish, ducks, and frogs live in ponds.

K SPELLING

Read the sentence with the missing word. Then find the correct way to spell the word, and fill in the circle next to your answer.

1. Carmen _____ Simon take a long walk every Sunday. *(words that end with nd, ng, or nk)*

   ○ a. an

   ○ b. ant

   ● c. and

   ○ d. angry

2. They _____ looking at nature. *(vowel-consonant-e spellings)*

   ● a. like

   ○ b. lyke

   ○ c. lik

   ○ d. lky

3. Simon points to a spider's _____ . *(short vowels)*

   ○ a. wehb

   ● b. web

   ○ c. weeb

   ○ d. webe

Go on ⇨

4. "Did you hear the goose _____?" asks

   Carmen. *(words that end with* nd, ng, *or* nk*)*

   ○ a. hank

   ● b. honk

   ○ c. hahnk

   ○ d. hawnk

5. There are _____ swimming in the stream! *(short vowels)*

   ○ a. fysh

   ○ b. fich

   ○ c. fishe

   ● d. fish

6. A frog is sitting on the big _____ . *(short vowels)*

   ● a. rock

   ○ b. rahk

   ○ c. roch

   ○ d. rocke

7. The children don't get too _____ . They

   might scare him. *(vowel-consonant-*e *spellings)*

   ○ a. cloze

   ○ b. clos

   ● c. close

   ○ d. cloce

Go on ⟹

8. "Listen to those birds _____ !" says Carmen.
   (words that end with nd, ng, *or* nk*)*

   ○ a. syng
   ○ b. sieng
   ○ c. siing
   ● d. sing

9. "Look at that frog! Did you see

   him _____ ?" asks Simon. *(short vowels)*

   ○ a. jemp
   ● b. jump
   ○ c. jomp
   ○ d. jumm

10. Carmen says, "I had fun, Simon. _____ you."
    (words that end with nd, ng, *or* nk*)*

    ○ a. Thang
    ○ b. Than
    ● c. Thank
    ○ d. Thak

Stop

GRAMMAR

Read each question and fill in the circle next to the best answer.

1. Which sentence is a **telling sentence**? *(telling sentences)*

- ● a. I want to go to an island.
- ○ b. Do you want to go to an island?
- ○ c. Have you ever been to an island?
- ○ d. Is that an island?

2. Which sentence is an **exclamation**? *(exclamations)*

- ○ a. Is it far from here?
- ○ b. It is two miles away.
- ● c. I can't wait to get there!
- ○ d. We will be there soon.

3. Which sentence **asks a question**? *(questions)*

- ○ a. I will look around on the island.
- ● b. What will I see on the island?
- ○ c. There are so many things to see on an island!
- ○ d. I might see many things on an island.

4. Which one is a **complete sentence**? *(complete sentences)*

- ○ a. Trees and sand.
- ○ b. On the island.
- ● c. I will see trees and sand on the island.
- ○ d. Trees and sand on the island.

5. Which is a **naming word**? *(naming words)*

- ○ a. see
- ● b. island
- ○ c. have
- ○ d. pretty

Stop

Name _____

 STUDY SKILLS *(following directions)*

**Read the directions. Then read each question and
fill in the circle next to the best answer.**

How to Make a Bird Feeder

It is fun to watch birds eat. Here is an easy
way to make a bird feeder.

1. Find a pine cone.
2. Tie a string around it.
3. Put some fat on the cone with a spoon.
4. Roll the cone in birdseed.
5. Hang up the feeder where birds can get to it.

---

1. What do you need to make this bird feeder?

- ○ a. rocks, glass jar, water, sand
- ○ b. ink, pen, boxes, clay
- ● c. pine cone, string, fat, birdseed
- ○ d. wood, plants, nails, sunlight

2. How many steps are there to make this bird
feeder?

- ○ a. four
- ○ b. two
- ○ c. one
- ● d. five

3. What is the **first** thing you must do to make this bird feeder?

- ○ a. Hang it up where birds can get to it.
- ● b. Find a pine cone.
- ○ c. Roll the cone in birdseed.
- ○ d. Tie a string around a pine cone.

4. What is the **last** thing you do when you make this bird feeder?

- ○ a. Find a pine cone.
- ○ b. Tie a string around it.
- ○ c. Put some fat on the cone.
- ● d. Hang up the feeder where birds can get to it.

5. What might happen if you did step 4 **before** step 3?

- ○ a. The birds wouldn't like seeds.
- ● b. The birdseed would not stick to the cone.
- ○ c. The string wouldn't stay on.
- ○ d. You would not have a place to hang the feeder.

Stop

GOOD FRIENDS
LEVEL 2, THEME 3
Theme Skills Test Record

Student _____ Date _____

STUDENT RECORD FORM	Possible Score	Criterion Score	Student Score
Part A: Author's Viewpoint	5	4	
Part B: Making Generalizations	5	4	
Part C: Making Judgments	5	4	
Part D: Cause and Effect	5	4	
Part E: Vowel Pairs: *ai, ay*	5	4	
Part F: Vowel Pairs: *ea, ee*	5	4	
Part G: Vowel Pairs: *oa, ow*	5	4	
Part H: Vowel Pair *ou;* Contractions	5	4	
Part I: High-Frequency Words	5	4	
Part J: Writing	5	4	
Part K: Spelling	10	8	
Part L: Grammar	5	4	
Part M: Study Skills	5	4	
TOTAL	70	56	
		Total Student Score x 1.42 =	%

Name _____

AUTHOR'S VIEWPOINT

Read this story. Then read each question and fill in the circle next to the best answer.

Rainy Day Fun

I always have fun on rainy days. That's because my mom lets me invite a friend over to play. Then she lets us have fun! My mom doesn't care too much about messes on rainy days, as long as we clean them up!

Sometimes my friend and I make play houses. We move the chairs in the dining room all around. Then we put sheets over them. We play like we are out in the woods.

Other times we make finger paintings. We try not to get paint all over. The paintings feel wet and slick. They make me think about the rain outside and how glad I am to be inside!

Go on ⟹

On some rainy days we bake cookies. My mom likes oatmeal cookies. I didn't always like them. Now I think they are pretty good. Baking cookies makes a big mess, but we get to eat cookies as we clean up.

It's nice to play with a friend on a rainy day. My mom is a good friend. She makes it a lot of fun for me.

1. What does the author think about rainy days?

   ○ a. They are boring and sad.
   ● b. They are good for playing with a friend.
   ○ c. They are good for walking your dog.
   ○ d. They are good for watching TV.

2. How does the author feel about his mom?

   ● a. She is a good friend.
   ○ b. She is in a bad mood.
   ○ c. She likes a big mess.
   ○ d. She makes too many rules.

Go on ⟹

3. What does the author think about going outside in the rain?

- ○ a. It is fun to jump in the water.
- ○ b. It is good to get wet.
- ○ c. It is fun to walk in the rain.
- ● d. He is glad to stay indoors.

4. What did the author change his mind about?

- ○ a. making play houses
- ○ b. finger painting
- ● c. oatmeal cookies
- ○ d. his mom

5. How does the author feel about making messes?

- ● a. It is fun.
- ○ b. It is not good.
- ○ c. It is boring.
- ○ d. It is too silly.

MAKING GENERALIZATIONS

Read this story. Then read the sentences and questions that follow it. Fill in the circle next to the best answer.

Making New Friends

It was Angelo's first day at his new school. His dad was walking to school with him.

"Do you think that the children here are nice?" asked Angelo.

"I'm sure they are," said his dad. "I've met some of the mothers and fathers, and they are nice."

"Do you think the children will like me?" asked Angelo.

"I'm sure they will," said his dad. They saw some children playing kickball. "See, they like to play kickball just like you."

"Do you think I'll make a friend today?" asked Angelo.

Go on

"I think you will," his dad said. "Angelo, I know that the first day at a new school can make you feel afraid. When I was about your age, I had to do it too. I really wanted to make a friend. And I did. You will too. To make friends, just be yourself. Be the first one to be nice. Ask the other children if they want to play. I bet they'll say yes."

"I'll do that, Dad." Then Angelo walked off to meet his new friends.

1. To make friends, you should _____ .

   ○ a. never go to a new school
   ● b. be the first one to be nice
   ○ c. look like you don't care
   ○ d. sit by yourself and wait

2. If you are going to a new school, you might feel _____ .

   ○ a. sleepy
   ○ b. old
   ● c. afraid
   ○ d. awake

Go on

3. Why does Angelo's dad think the children will be nice?

- ○ a. Their rooms are clean.
- ○ b. The town looks nice.
- ○ c. They go to Angelo's school.
- ● d. The mothers and fathers are nice.

4. Why does Angelo's dad think the children will like Angelo?

- ● a. They like to play kickball, and so does Angelo.
- ○ b. They have a nice school.
- ○ c. He walked him to school.
- ○ d. He is new to the school.

5. Which sentence can you tell is true about Angelo's dad?

- ○ a. He does not like the new school.
- ○ b. He is late for work.
- ○ c. He likes to play football.
- ● d. He cares about Angelo.

C MAKING JUDGMENTS

Read this story. Then read each question and fill in the circle next to the best answer.

Something New

Sally's mom took Sally and her friends Jenna and Parris out to eat. "Let's try something new," said Sally's mom. All the kids said that would be fun. "Bean soup for everyone!" said Sally's mom.

When the soup came, the children looked at it for a while.

"I don't think I will like this," said Sally. "It looks funny."

"I don't think I will like it if Sally doesn't," said Parris.

"Well, it smells good to me," said Jenna. "I'm going to try it." Jenna took a sip of the soup. "It's different," she said. "I don't like it as much as my mom's soup, but this soup is good."

Sally's mom asked Parris and Sally if they were going to try the soup.

Go on ⟹

"Since Jenna doesn't think it's too bad, I'll try it," said Parris.

"Me too," said Sally.

"Good for you," said Sally's mom. "You all tried something new."

1. Why did Sally think she wouldn't like bean soup?

   ○ a. Jenna didn't like it.
   ○ b. Parris didn't like it.
   ○ c. Her mom didn't like it.
   ● d. It looked funny.

2. Why did Parris think he wouldn't like bean soup?

   ● a. Sally didn't think she would like it.
   ○ b. He doesn't eat soup.
   ○ c. He had tried it before.
   ○ d. He only likes to eat bread.

Go on

3. Why did Jenna go ahead and try the bean soup?

- ○ a. It looked like her mom's soup.
- ● b. It smelled good to her.
- ○ c. She had tried it before.
- ○ d. Sally's mom liked it.

4. What did Jenna think about bean soup after she tried it?

- ● a. It was good, but not as good as her mom's soup.
- ○ b. It was the one she liked best of all.
- ○ c. It tasted the same as her mom's soup.
- ○ d. She did not like it.

5. Why did Sally and Parris try the bean soup at the end of the story?

- ○ a. It smelled good.
- ○ b. Sally's mom liked it.
- ● c. Jenna liked it.
- ○ d. They wanted to try something new.

Stop

CAUSE AND EFFECT

Read this story. Then read each question and fill in the circle next to the best answer.

Fun at the Park

Cliff and Nita were best friends. They had fun playing together at the park on sunny days.

One day Nita was pushing Cliff on the swing. Three small children were waiting with their moms. "Let's let one of those children swing now," said Cliff.

"That was nice, Cliff," said Nita. "Anyway, I want to eat. Let's ask my dad if we can have our lunch now."

Just then, rain started to come down hard.

"Come on!" said Nita's dad. "Run! Get in the car."

Cliff and Nita started running. Cliff wasn't looking where he was going. He bumped into a little boy. "Are you all right?" said Cliff. The little boy was fine, so Cliff and Nita went on.

When they were in out of the rain, Nita's dad gave them their lunch. "Have you ever had to eat at the park in a car before?" he asked. He made a silly face.

The kids grinned. They were having fun at the park, even if it was raining.

1. Why did Cliff stop swinging?

- ○ a. It was time for Nita to swing.
- ○ b. It was raining.
- ● c. Other children were waiting.
- ○ d. He was tired.

2. Why did Nita say, "That was nice, Cliff"?

- ○ a. She wanted to go home.
- ○ b. Cliff asked for food.
- ● c. Cliff let another child take a turn on the swings.
- ○ d. She wanted to see her dad.

3. Why did Cliff bump into the little boy?

- ○ a. It was raining.
- ○ b. Cliff could not swing.
- ○ c. Nita's dad called to them.
- ● d. Cliff wasn't looking where he was going.

4. Why did Nita, her dad, and Cliff get in the car?

- ● a. It was raining.
- ○ b. They wanted to go home.
- ○ c. They wanted to have lunch.
- ○ d. It was getting dark.

5. Why did Nita and Cliff grin at the end of the story?

- ○ a. Nita's dad got out their food.
- ● b. Nita's dad made a silly face.
- ○ c. Nita's dad said they had to go home.
- ○ d. Nita's dad played in the rain.

E VOWEL PAIRS (ai, ay)

Read the sentences. Think about what word might go in the blank. Fill in the circle next to the right answer.

1. Donald, Maria, and Michael were good friends. They would _____ together all the time.
   (vowel pair ay*)*
   - ○ a. plus
   - ● b. play
   - ○ c. last
   - ○ d. tray

2. Then Maria moved _____ . Donald and Michael missed her. They had a present to send her. *(vowel pair* ay*)*
   - ○ a. made
   - ○ b. very
   - ○ c. ray
   - ● d. away

3. "Should we run away with the present? We could ride the _____ ," said Michael.
   (vowel pair ai*)*
   - ● a. train
   - ○ b. bait
   - ○ c. trim
   - ○ d. tan

Go on ⟩

4. "Don't be silly, Michael," said Donald. "Use your _____ ." *(vowel pair* ai*)*

- ○ a. pad
- ○ b. bran
- ● c. brain
- ○ d. rain

5. "I guess you are right," said Michael. "We should send it in the _____ ." *(vowel pair* ai*)*

- ○ a. mall
- ○ b. rain
- ○ c. may
- ● d. mail

F

VOWEL PAIRS *(ea, ee)*

Read the sentences. Think about what word might go in the blank. Then fill in the circle next to the right answer.

1. "Come on, Cara!" said Grandfather. "Get into the car." Cara ran to the car. She slid onto the

   _____ . *(vowel pair ea)*

   ○ a. set
   ○ b. wheat
   ● c. seat
   ○ d. sat

2. "Don't forget that we _____ to pick up Josh, Grandfather. You said I could take a friend to the store with us," said Cara. *(vowel pair ee)*

   ● a. need
   ○ b. thread
   ○ c. bead
   ○ d. Ned

Go on

3. "We're on our way," said Grandfather. "I'm going to get each of you a _____ at the store." *(vowel pair* ea*)*

   ○ a. head
   ○ b. read
   ○ c. trade
   ● d. treat

4. Josh jumped into the car. "Grandfather says we can get something _____ at the store," Cara told Josh. *(vowel pair* ee*)*

   ○ a. weed
   ● b. sweet
   ○ c. read
   ○ d. head

5. "You can only have _____ and butter," Grandfather joked. "Oh, Grandfather!" said Cara. *(vowel pair* ea*)*

   ○ a. braid
   ○ b. thread
   ● c. bread
   ○ d. head

G

VOWEL PAIRS *(oa, ow)*

Read the sentences. Think about what word might go in the blank. Fill in the circle next to your answer.

1. "What can we play?" asked Dolores. "I know!" said Reva. "Let's make a _____ with a big sail!" *(vowel pair oa)*

   ○ a. glow
   ○ b. bit
   ○ c. croak
   ● d. boat

2. "We have no wood," said Dolores. "And we can't go to _____ to get any. What will we make it from?" *(vowel pair ow)*

   ● a. town
   ○ b. frown
   ○ c. tone
   ○ d. yellow

3. " _____ me," said Reva as she went into the house. She asked her mom for a stick. Then she asked Dolores to cut out a sail. *(vowel pair* ow*)*

   ○ a. Hollow
   ○ b. Fall
   ● c. Follow
   ○ d. Goat

4. Reva put the sail on the stick. Then she pushed the stick into a bar of _____ . *(vowel pair* oa*)*

   ○ a. owl
   ● b. soap
   ○ c. gown
   ○ d. soup

5. The girls wanted to test what they had made. Dolores put it into water in the bathtub. "Look at it _____ !" the friends cried. *(vowel pair* oa*)*

   ○ a. flat
   ○ b. coat
   ● c. float
   ○ d. growl

VOWEL PAIR (ou) CONTRACTIONS

Read the sentences. Think about what word might go in the blank. Fill in the circle next to the right answer.

1. Jeff and Mitchell walked on the beach. "Look at the shell I _____ !" said Mitchell. *(vowel pair* ou*)*

- ○ a. food
- ○ b. couch
- ● c. found
- ○ d. flower

2. They picked up more shells and put them into _____ . They put all the brown ones together. They put all the pink ones together. *(vowel pair* ou*)*

- ● a. groups
- ○ b. grapes
- ○ c. greens
- ○ d. sounds

Go on ⇒

3. "What _____ we do about this one?" asked
   Mitchell. "It is brown **and** pink." *(vowel pair* ou)

   ○ a. house
   ○ b. showed
   ○ c. you
   ● d. should

4. "_____ not sure," said Jeff. Then he picked
   up another brown and pink shell. *(contractions)*

   ○ a. Aren't
   ○ b. Don't
   ● c. I'm
   ○ d. That's

5. "Now _____ easy! We can put the two
   brown and pink ones together," said Jeff. *(contractions)*

   ○ a. can't
   ○ b. he'll
   ○ c. you've
   ● d. it's

HIGH-FREQUENCY WORDS

Read the sentences. Think about what word might go in the blank. Fill in the circle next to the right answer.

1. Tomás and his family were going to take a trip. "You're my best friend, Tomás," said Lynn. "I'm sure going to _____ you."

    ○ a. black
    ○ b. ever
    ○ c. still
    ● d. miss

2. "What will you do _____ I am gone?" asked Tomás.

    ○ a. round
    ○ b. through
    ○ c. last
    ● d. while

Go on

3. "I don't know," said Lynn. "I might have to play by _____ ."

- ● a. myself
- ○ b. both
- ○ c. girl
- ○ d. still

4. "I _____ you could go too," said Tomás.

- ○ a. last
- ○ b. soon
- ● c. wish
- ○ d. boy

5. Tomás had an idea. He ran home and asked his mom if Lynn could go on the trip. "Of course," said his mom. "I'll talk to Lynn's mom and dad." Tomás thought it was the _____ idea he had ever had!

- ○ a. round
- ● b. best
- ○ c. blue
- ○ d. ever

Stop

J

WRITING *(writing clearly with nouns)*

Read each sentence. Find the exact noun that should replace the underlined words. Then fill in the circle next to the right answer.

1. Jared wanted to ask <u>a friend</u> to go skating.

   - ○ a. faster
   - ● b. Rosa
   - ○ c. Silver Street
   - ○ d. girl

2. He called and asked if she could go on <u>a day</u>.

   - ● a. Friday
   - ○ b. week
   - ○ c. Chicago
   - ○ d. Jessica

3. She said she could go. She asked if Jared could pick her up at her grandmother's house. "It is by <u>a park</u>," she said.

   - ○ a. Randy
   - ○ b. road
   - ● c. Grant Park
   - ○ d. beach

 **Go on**

4. "That's on the way to <u>a place</u>," said Jared.
"We'll be there at three o'clock."

- ○ a. animals
- ○ b. people
- ○ c. a thing
- ● d. the skating rink

5. "Thanks, Jared," she said. "I can't wait. I want
you to meet <u>a person</u>."

- ● a. my grandmother
- ○ b. street
- ○ c. June Bug Drive
- ○ d. Bayside School

SPELLING

Read the sentence with the missing word. Then find the correct way to spell the word and fill in the circle next to your answer.

1. Joey called Aunt Ruth and said, "May I _____ bring a friend to your farm?" *(long e spellings with* ee *and* ea*)*

○ a. pleese

○ b. plese

● c. please

○ d. pliez

2. "Of course!" said Aunt Ruth. "But it may _____ soon." *(long a spellings with* ai *and* ay*)*

○ a. roan

● b. rain

○ c. ran

○ d. rane

3. "If it does, we will stay inside with the animals," said Joey. "May we _____ the goats?" *(long e spellings with* ee *and* ea*)*

○ a. fead

○ b. fede

○ c. feade

● d. feed

4. " _____ see," said Aunt Ruth. *(contractions)*

   ● a. We'll
   ○ b. Weel
   ○ c. Weal
   ○ d. W'll

5. "Thanks, Aunt Ruth," said Joey. "I can't wait to
   _____ Monica your farm." *(long o spellings with* oa *and* ow*)*

   ○ a. shol
   ○ b. shoa
   ● c. show
   ○ d. shou

6. The next _____ was bright and clear. Aunt
   Ruth said, "I'm happy you came!" *(long a spellings with* ai *and* ay*)*

   ○ a. daay
   ○ b. dai
   ● c. day
   ○ d. daye

7. Joey and Monica picked some flowers, and
   Aunt Ruth put them in a _____ . *(long o spellings with* oa *and* ow*)*

   ○ a. bawl
   ● b. bowl
   ○ c. bowal
   ○ d. bowll

Go on ⇒

8. They got to pet one of the sheep. It had a
   thick _____ . *(long o spellings with oa and ow)*

   ● a. coat
   ○ b. coot
   ○ c. cote
   ○ d. coate

9. All the crops were growing well. The grass
   was tall and _____ . *(long e spellings with ee and ea)*

   ○ a. greene
   ○ b. grene
   ○ c. grean
   ● d. green

10. At the end of the day, Joey and Monica
    _____ want to go home. *(contractions)*

    ○ a. dident
    ● b. didn't
    ○ c. did'nt
    ○ d. didnt'

GRAMMAR

Choose the word that correctly completes the sentence. Fill in the circle next to your answer.

1. Donna and Shirenda were out on the playground. They were wearing their new spring _____ . *(one and more than one)*

   ○ a. dress'
   ○ b. dressx
   ● c. dresses
   ○ d. dress's

2. Another girl came over to play. Her name was _____ . *(special nouns)*

   ○ a. andrea
   ○ b. ANDREA
   ○ c. girl
   ● d. Andrea

3. The three girls talked about things they liked to do. _____ all liked to jump rope. *(words for nouns)*

   ○ a. She
   ● b. They
   ○ c. It
   ○ d. He

Go on ⟹

4. "Do you jump on one foot or on both

   _____ ?" asked Donna. *(nouns that change spelling)*

   - ● a. feet
   - ○ b. foot
   - ○ c. foots
   - ○ d. footes

5. "I can jump on one foot using two _____ ,"
   said Shirenda. The girls thought that was
   funny! They knew they would all have fun
   together. *(one and more than one)*

   - ○ a. rope
   - ● b. ropes
   - ○ c. ropess
   - ○ d. rope's

STUDY SKILLS *(glossary)*

Look at the glossary entry. Then read each question. Fill in the circle next to your answer.

> **far** a long way off: *Timothy lived **far** from town.*

1. Which of the following is **not** part of a glossary entry?

- ○ a. the meaning of the word
- ○ b. the spelling of the word
- ○ c. an example sentence using the word
- ● d. page numbers

2. What does the word **far** mean?

- ○ a. right next to
- ○ b. under the water
- ● c. a long way off
- ○ d. easy to find

3. Which of the following could be another example sentence for the word **far**?

- ○ a. Janet tried to far the ball.
- ● b. Alex sailed far across the sea.
- ○ c. Please far the door.
- ○ d. I saw a good far today.

4. Which entry word would you find **before** the entry for the word **far**?

- ● a. each
- ○ b. rest
- ○ c. place
- ○ d. watch

5. Which entry word would you find **after** the entry for the word **far**?

- ○ a. about
- ○ b. ever
- ● c. price
- ○ d. close

FAMILY PHOTOS
LEVEL 2, THEME 4
Theme Skills Test Record

Student _____ Date _____

STUDENT RECORD FORM	Possible Score	Criterion Score	Student Score
Part A: Categorize and Classify	5	4	
Part B: Inferences: Making Predictions	5	4	
Part C: Sequence	5	4	
Part D: Story Structure and Summarizing	5	4	
Part E: Vowel Pairs *oo, ew, ue*	5	4	
Part F: *r-* and *l-*Controlled Vowels	5	4	
Part G: Base Words, Prefixes, and Endings (*re-, dis-, un-; -ed, -ing, -er, -est*)	5	4	
Part H: High-Frequency Words	5	4	
Part I: Writing	5	4	
Part J: Spelling	10	8	
Part K: Grammar	5	4	
Part L: Study Skills	5	4	
TOTAL	65	52	
Total Student Score x 1.54 =			%

CATEGORIZE AND CLASSIFY

Read this story. Then read each question and fill in the circle next to the best answer.

Grandma made Grace a green cap. Grace wore her cap to school every day. But one day, when it was time to go home, Grace could not find her cap.

"Look in the Lost and Found Box," said Grace's teacher.

Grace began to dig into the box. She pulled out a boot, a coat, and a kite. Then she pulled out a book, a shoe, and a pen. "I don't see my cap," said Grace. "Grandma will be sad if I've lost it."

Grace kept digging. She pulled out a blue hat and a pencil. She pulled out a watch, a shirt, and a lunch box. "This box is almost empty," said Grace as she pulled out a doll. Then she looked into the box. "I see my green cap!" said Grace.

1. **Which thing from the box is most like a shoe?**
   - ○ a. a pen
   - ● b. a boot
   - ○ c. a hat
   - ○ d. a watch

Go on ⟹

2. Which two things from the box are clothes?

  ○ a. a doll and a shoe
  ○ b. a book and a cap
  ● c. a shirt and a coat
  ○ d. a kite and a lunch box

3. Which thing from the box is most like a pen?

  ○ a. a shirt
  ● b. a pencil
  ○ c. a kite
  ○ d. a hat

4. Which two things from the box are toys?

  ○ a. a pen and a book
  ○ b. a lunch box and a boot
  ○ c. a shoe and a coat
  ● d. a kite and a doll

5. Which thing from the box is most like a cap?

  ● a. a hat
  ○ b. a pencil
  ○ c. a watch
  ○ d. a doll

B

INFERENCES: MAKING PREDICTIONS

Read each story. Then read the question that follows. Fill in the circle next to the best answer.

Grandpa was coming for a visit. Dad and Mary went to meet Grandpa's train. They watched the people getting off the train. At last they saw Grandpa. He smiled and waved at them.

1. What do you think will happen next?

○ a. Mary and Dad will take a train ride.

● b. Dad and Mary will take Grandpa to their house.

○ c. Grandpa will get back on the train.

○ d. They will go to Grandpa's house.

Lupe and Manuel found some old clothes that Mama and Papa didn't wear anymore. "Mama, may we have these clothes?" asked Lupe and Manuel.

"Yes, you may," said Mama.

2. What do you think will happen next?

○ a. Mama will put on her old clothes.

● b. Lupe and Manuel will play dress-up.

○ c. Lupe and Manuel will buy new clothes.

○ d. Mama will put the clothes away.

Go on ⇒

"The apples on our tree are ripe," said Jamal. "I'll pick some and take them to Aunt Ruby."

Aunt Ruby smiled when she saw the apples. "What a nice thing to do," she said to Jamal. "You should have a treat." With that, Aunt Ruby began to make some apple pies.

3. What do you think will happen next?

- ○ a. Aunt Ruby will eat the apples.
- ○ b. Jamal will take some apples home with him.
- ● c. Aunt Ruby will give Jamal an apple pie.
- ○ d. Jamal will pick more apples.

Dad and Leah were looking for their cat, Tiger. She had been missing for days. At last, Dad and Leah found Tiger under a bush. They found two new kittens, too.

"Tiger should stay here with her kittens for a while," said Dad. "But I'm sure she's very hungry."

4. What do you think will happen next?

- ○ a. Leah will take Tiger home.
- ○ b. Tiger will find some new kittens.
- ○ c. Dad will take the kittens home.
- ● d. Leah will bring Tiger some food.

Go on ▷

Mom came home with some pictures. "These are pictures of Uncle Luke's visit," she told Meg.

Meg and Mom looked at the pictures together. "Here is a nice picture of you and Uncle Luke," said Mom. "He would like to have that picture."

5. What do you think will happen next?

- ● a. Meg will send the picture to Uncle Luke.
- ○ b. Meg and Mom will go on a trip.
- ○ c. Meg will hang the picture in her room.
- ○ d. Mom will take a picture of Meg.

Stop

SEQUENCE

Read this story. Then read each question and fill in the circle next to the best answer.

Dad was waiting for Tim after school. Tim was surprised. "It's going to rain," said Dad. "I didn't want you to get wet walking home."

The rain started as Dad and Tim drove away. When they got home, they ran to the house. The door was locked. Dad looked for his key, but he couldn't find it. Dad and Tim stood in the rain. They were getting wet. "I'll open the window," said Dad. "You slide in and open the door."

Tim slid through the open window. Then he let Dad inside. Tim and Dad looked at each other and laughed. Their dripping clothes were making puddles on the floor.

Dad and Tim changed their clothes. Next they mopped up the puddles. Then Dad dried Tim's hair. "I'm sorry you got wet," he said.

"That's okay, Dad," said Tim. "But next time, bring your key."

1. What happened first in the story?
   - ● a. Dad was waiting for Tim.
   - ○ b. Tim called Dad to pick him up.
   - ○ c. Dad said, "It's raining."
   - ○ d. Dad and Tim drove away.

2. What happened before Dad and Tim got home?

- ○ a. Dad dried Tim's hair.
- ● b. It started to rain.
- ○ c. Dad stopped to buy a mop.
- ○ d. Dad and Tim laughed at each other.

3. What happened after Dad and Tim ran to the house?

- ○ a. Tim fell into a puddle.
- ○ b. Dad and Tim ran back to the car.
- ○ c. Dad opened the door for Tim.
- ● d. Dad looked for his key.

4. When did Tim let Dad inside the house?

- ○ a. after he changed his clothes
- ○ b. after he made dinner
- ● c. after he slid through the window
- ○ d. when he found his key

5. What happened last in the story?

- ○ a. Tim and Dad watched the rain.
- ○ b. Tim and Dad changed their clothes.
- ○ c. Tim locked the door.
- ● d. Tim told Dad to bring his key next time.

Stop

D

STORY STRUCTURE AND SUMMARIZING

Read this story. Then read each question and fill in the circle next to the best answer.

When it was time for Show and Tell, Mrs. Chang asked Joey to go first.

"I can't," said Joey. "My surprise isn't here yet."

Mrs. Chang called on Ahmed. He showed a picture of a boat he rode in last summer. Then Gina showed a rock she found in the woods.

Joey wasn't watching. He was wishing his surprise would come.

Next Bruce showed the class a clay pot he made. Then Tia showed everyone her new drum.

"I hope my surprise gets here soon," thought Joey.

Just then there was a knock on the door. Joey's mother walked in. She was carrying Joey's new baby sister. Joey took the baby in his arms. "This is my new sister, Emmy," he told the class. "She's what I have for Show and Tell."

1. Where does this story take place?

- ○ a. in the woods
- ○ b. on a boat
- ○ c. at Joey's house
- ● d. at school

2. Who is this story mostly about?

○ a. Mrs. Chang
○ b. Ahmed
● c. Joey
○ d. Tia

3. What were the boys and girls doing in this story?

○ a. They were drawing pictures.
○ b. They were making clay pots.
○ c. They were playing drums.
● d. They were having Show and Tell.

4. What is the problem in this story?

● a. Joey couldn't take his turn until his surprise came.
○ b. Joey was feeling shy.
○ c. Joey didn't like his surprise.
○ d. Mrs. Chang didn't call on Joey.

5. What happened at the end of this story?

○ a. Joey never took his turn.
● b. Joey showed his baby sister to the class.
○ c. Bruce showed his clay pot.
○ d. Joey wished his surprise would come.

Stop

E

VOWEL PAIRS *(oo, ew, ue)*

Read each sentence and think about what word might go in the blank. Then fill in the circle next to the best answer.

1. Ali and her dad planted a tree. The tree _____ to be tall. *(ew)*

   ○ a. blow
   ● b. grew
   ○ c. green
   ○ d. grow

2. One day Ali and her dad sat in the _____ shade under the tree. *(oo)*

   ○ a. call
   ○ b. set
   ○ c. coal
   ● d. cool

3. All at once a _____ and white bird came out of the tree. *(ue)*

   ● a. blue
   ○ b. blink
   ○ c. beep
   ○ d. blow

Go on ⟹

4. "That bird has baby birds," said Dad. "She will find _____ for them." *(oo)*

   ○ a. left
   ○ b. for
   ● c. food
   ○ d. soft

5. Ali went inside and _____ a picture of the bird in the tree. *(ew)*

   ○ a. spot
   ● b. drew
   ○ c. net
   ○ d. drank

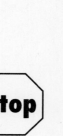

r- AND l-CONTROLLED VOWELS

Read the following sentences and think about what word might go in the blank. Then fill in the circle next to the best answer.

1. Sam and Li went to the _____ to play in the snow.
   - ○ a. pork
   - ○ b. pet
   - ● c. park
   - ○ d. poke

2. It was very cold out. "I wish I had _____ like a dog," said Li.
   - ● a. fur
   - ○ b. for
   - ○ c. far
   - ○ d. tall

3. "Those kids are making a snowman," said Sam. "Let's _____ them."
   - ○ a. heap
   - ○ b. here
   - ● c. help
   - ○ d. hour

4. Sam and Li made a big _____ of snow.

○ a. bake

● b. ball

○ c. take

○ d. back

5. "This is hard work!" said Sam. "My arms
_____ ."

○ a. hit

○ b. hall

○ c. hut

● d. hurt

Stop

BASE WORDS, PREFIXES, AND ENDINGS

(re-, dis-, un-; -ed, -ing, -er, -est)

Read the following sentences and think about what word might go in the blank. Then fill in the circle next to the best answer.

1. "The mess in your room makes me _____ ," said Mama.

   ○ a. dishappy
   ● b. unhappy
   ○ c. happied
   ○ d. rehappy

2. "What made my plant fall over? Now I have to _____ it," said Sarah.

   ○ a. plants
   ○ b. planted
   ● c. replant
   ○ d. planting

3. Mama said, "Your little brother was _____ in your room. He must have done it."

   ○ a. play
   ○ b. plays
   ● c. playing
   ○ d. played

Go on ⇨

4. "I _____ it when he makes a mess in my room," said Sarah.

- ○ a. unliked
- ○ b. liking
- ○ c. likes
- ● d. dislike

5. "If he had _____ to play with my things," said Sarah, "I wouldn't be so mad."

- ● a. asked
- ○ b. asking
- ○ c. asks
- ○ d. asker

H HIGH-FREQUENCY WORDS

Read the following sentences and think about what word might go in the blank. Then fill in the circle next to the best answer.

1. Gran _____ Tanya a surprise. She carried it into the house.

   ○ a. notice
   ○ b. clean
   ○ c. warm
   ● d. brought

2. "I saw this dog _____ ," Gran said. "I thought I should buy him for you."

   ● a. today
   ○ b. full
   ○ c. done
   ○ d. few

3. "He's not a puppy. He's nearly one _____ old," said Gran.

   ○ a. fall
   ○ b. world
   ○ c. word
   ● d. year

4. "His fur is all _____ ," Tanya said. "I will call him Snowball."

     ○ a. four

     ○ b. mean

     ● c. white

     ○ d. shout

5. "Stay right there with Snowball," said Gran. "I'm going to take a _____ of you."

     ○ a. second

     ● b. picture

     ○ c. light

     ○ d. laugh

WRITING

Find the complete sentence and fill in the circle next to your answer. *(writing complete sentences)*

1. ○ a. Sofia and the ice-cream shop after school.

   ○ b. On her way home from school.

   ○ c. Stopped at the ice-cream shop after school.

   ● d. Sofia stopped at the ice-cream shop after school.

2. ○ a. To get a treat for her father.

   ● b. She wanted to get a treat for her father.

   ○ c. A treat for her father.

   ○ d. She wanted to get a treat for.

3. ○ a. Left the shop with a big ice-cream cone.

   ○ b. The shop with a big ice-cream cone.

   ● c. She left the shop with a big ice-cream cone.

   ○ d. She left the shop with.

Read the sentence. Find the verb that tells you the most. Fill in the circle next to your answer.

(writing clearly with verbs)

4. As Sofia walked home, the ice-cream cone
_____ on the ground.

- ● a. plopped
- ○ b. went
- ○ c. goes
- ○ d. was

5. "Oh, no!" Sofia _____ . "Now I'll have to buy another ice-cream cone."

- ○ a. said
- ● b. shouted
- ○ c. says
- ○ d. asked

Stop

SPELLING

Read the sentence with the missing word. Then find the correct way to spell the word, and fill in the circle next to your answer.

1. "Let's go fishing _____ we clean the house," said Aunt Lena. *(words that end with -er)*

   ○ a. aftr
   ○ b. afta
   ● c. after
   ○ d. afte

2. My _____ Ben and I were excited. *(words that end with -er)*

   ● a. brother
   ○ b. brouther
   ○ c. brather
   ○ d. brothr

3. We cleaned the house quickly and got ready _____ our trip. *(the vowel + r sound in store)*

   ○ a. fo
   ○ b. forr
   ○ c. far
   ● d. for

Go on

4. I brought along a _____ for us to read.

(the vowel sound in book*)*

- ○ a. bok
- ● b. book
- ○ c. boak
- ○ d. buk

5. Aunt Lena had to stop at the _____ to get

some worms. *(the vowel + r sound in* store*)*

- ○ a. sterr
- ● b. store
- ○ c. stor
- ○ d. star

6. We got to the river around _____ .

(the vowel sound in moon*)*

- ● a. noon
- ○ b. non
- ○ c. none
- ○ d. noone

7. We couldn't wait to _____ fishing.

(the vowel + r sound in car*)*

- ○ a. starr
- ○ b. starte
- ○ c. stort
- ● d. start

Go on ⟹

8. We fished until it got _____ . *(the vowel + r sound in* car*)*

- ○ a. darck
- ● b. dark
- ○ c. durk
- ○ d. dirk

9. Ben caught _____ fish than I did. *(the vowel + r sound in* store*)*

- ○ a. mer
- ○ b. mor
- ● c. more
- ○ d. moer

10. I hope we go fishing again very _____ . *(the vowel sound in* moon*)*

- ○ a. sune
- ○ b. son
- ○ c. sone
- ● d. soon

K GRAMMAR

Read the sentences and find the verb that should go in each blank. Then fill in the circle next to the best answer.

1. Eva made a shirt for her brother. When he got home, she _____ him to try it on. *(verbs with -ed)*

   ○ a. ask
   ○ b. asking
   ● c. asked
   ○ d. asks

2. Pablo put on the shirt. Then he said, "This shirt _____ too big for me." *(verbs that tell about now)*

   ○ a. looked
   ● b. looks
   ○ c. looking
   ○ d. look

3. Eva did not say a word, but she _____ a little upset. *(is/are, was/were)*

   ● a. was
   ○ b. is
   ○ c. are
   ○ d. were

Go on ⇨

4. Mama smiled at Eva. "I'll be happy if you
   _____ the shirt to me." *(verbs that tell about now)*

   ● a. give
   ○ b. gives
   ○ c. gived
   ○ d. giving

5. "That's true," said Eva. "The shirt _____ the
   right size for you!" *(is/are, was/were)*

   ○ a. are
   ○ b. were
   ● c. is
   ○ d. am

STUDY SKILLS *(maps)*

Look at the map. Then read each question and fill in the circle next to the best answer.

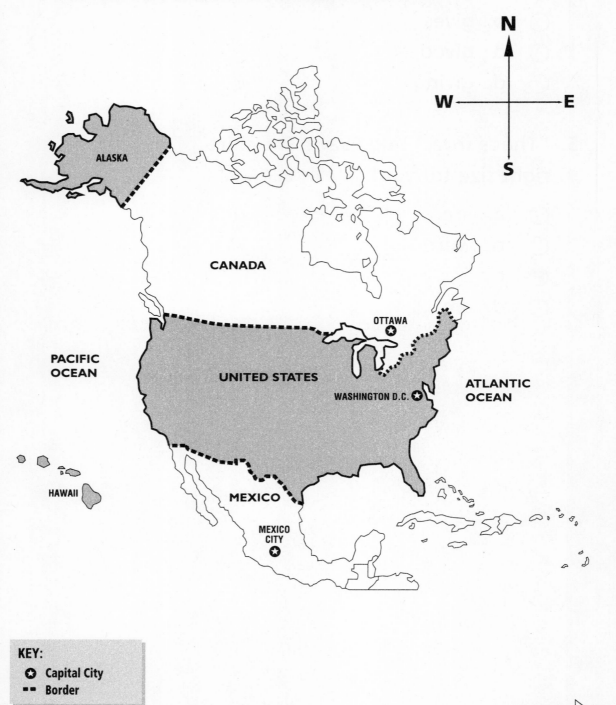

KEY:
⊙ Capital City
∎∎ Border

Go on ➡

1. What ocean is west of the United States?

○ a. Alaska
○ b. Atlantic Ocean
● c. Pacific Ocean
○ d. Mexico

2. What country is north of the United States?

● a. Canada
○ b. Mexico
○ c. Mexico City
○ d. Washington, D.C.

3. If you were in Canada and traveled directly south, what country would you have to pass through to get to Mexico?

○ a. Alaska
○ b. Hawaii
○ c. Mexico
● d. United States

Go on

4. What do the stars on the map show?

○ a. oceans
● b. capital cities
○ c. borders
○ d. land

5. How is the boundary between different countries shown?

○ a. stars
○ b. words
○ c. circles
● d. broken lines

THAT'S INCREDIBLE!

LEVEL 2, THEME 5

Theme Skills Test Record

Student _____ Date _____

STUDENT RECORD FORM	Possible Score	Criterion Score	Student Score
Part A: Noting Details	5	4	
Part B: Fantasy and Realism	5	4	
Part C: Fact and Opinion	5	4	
Part D: Base Words and Endings: *-s, -es, -ed, -ing*	5	4	
Part E: Vowel Pairs: *ow, ou*	5	4	
Part F: Suffixes *-ful, -ness, -ous, -ly, -y;* Words with *aw, al*	5	4	
Part G: High-Frequency Words	5	4	
Part H: Writing	5	4	
Part I: Spelling	10	8	
Part J: Grammar	5	4	
Part K: Study Skills	5	4	
TOTAL	60	48	
Total Student Score x 1.67 =			%

A NOTING DETAILS

Read this story. Then read each question and fill in the circle next to the best answer.

Incredible Treasure

Shawna opened the door and looked outside. She smiled when she saw Max waiting for her. She and Max liked to play by the stream. Today they were going to take a picnic. What fun! Shawna picked up the picnic cooler and ran out the door.

After their picnic they walked by the clear, cool water. "Let's pretend that we are looking for lost gold!" said Max. "We can dig in the dirt."

The two friends used spoons and sticks to dig in the wet dirt near the stream. All at once Max cried out, "Look what I found!" He pulled on something white and hard in the ground. Max and Shawna worked and worked, and at last they pulled the thing out of the dirt. It was about as long as Max's arm.

"Wait here," said Shawna. "I'll get someone to help us." She ran back home. Soon she came back with their teacher, Mr. Harris, who lived nearby.

Go on ⇒

"My goodness!" he exclaimed. "I think this is a dinosaur bone! This animal lived many, many years ago. And to think you found its bone right here!"

Max gave Shawna a big smile. "We didn't find gold," he said, "but I know we won't forget **this** day!"

1. What detail tells you Shawna is glad to see Max?

   ○ a. She opened the door.
   ● b. She smiled when she saw him waiting.
   ○ c. She went downstairs.
   ○ d. She picked up the picnic cooler.

2. How do you know Max and Shawna are friends?

   ● a. They like to play together by the stream.
   ○ b. They go to school together.
   ○ c. They live next door to each other.
   ○ d. They are brother and sister.

3. What details tell about the place where they found the bone?

   ○ a. It was far from home.
   ○ b. Grass was growing in the dirt.
   ● c. The dirt was wet near the stream.
   ○ d. The dirt was dry and hard.

4. What detail tells you how big the bone was?

   ○ a. It was in the dirt.
   ○ b. It could be dug up with a spoon.
   ○ c. It was hard and white.
   ● d. It was about as long as Max's arm.

5. How do you know Max and Shawna are happy about their day?

   ○ a. Shawna ran to her house.
   ○ b. Shawna returned with Mr. Harris.
   ● c. Max smiled and said they won't forget this day.
   ○ d. They wanted to find gold by the stream.

Stop

FANTASY AND REALISM

Read this story. Then read each question and fill in the circle next to the best answer.

A New Friend

Billy had just come to a new town. He had not found new friends yet, so he just went outside to play every day. One day he saw a bug sitting on a flower. The bug looked up at Billy and said, "Hello! My name is Tad. I am a wishing bug. I can make all your wishes come true."

"Wow!" said Billy. He picked Tad up and put the bug on his cap. "Let me see. What can I wish for?" Billy thought out loud. "I know. I want some cake." Poof! There was the cake.

"This is fun!" Billy sat down and ate the cake. Then he said, "Now I would like to fly."

"As you wish," said Tad. Poof! Billy was flying through the air. He looked down on the treetops. He saw the roof of his new house. He could see his mother working outside.

Tad said, "Don't fly too close to those birds. Birds like to eat bugs, you know."

Go on

After a while, Billy said he needed to go home. Right away, he was standing by his new house. "Thanks for a good time today," he said to Tad. He put the bug down on the grass. "I'll see you later."

The next day it rained, and Billy could not go outside. When it finally stopped raining, he ran outside and looked everywhere for Tad. Then Billy saw a rainbow in the sky. As he looked closer, he saw Tad. The bug had a big brush and was making the rainbow go all the way across the sky! Tad looked down and yelled, "Hi, Billy!"

Billy was happy that he had found his new friend again.

1. Which of these could not be real?
   - ○ a. a boy
   - ● b. a talking bug
   - ○ c. birds
   - ○ d. a boy's mother

Go on ⇨

2. Which of these things could happen in real life?

- ● a. A boy moves to a new town.
- ○ b. A boy finds a wishing bug.
- ○ c. The wishing bug tells the boy his name.
- ○ d. The bug makes wishes come true.

3. Which of these things could happen only in a made-up story?

- ○ a. A boy picks up a bug.
- ○ b. A boy puts a bug on his cap.
- ● c. A bug makes some cake show up from nowhere.
- ○ d. A boy sits down and eats some cake.

4. Which of these things could happen in real life?

- ○ a. A bug makes a boy fly.
- ○ b. A boy goes flying through the air.
- ○ c. A bug talks to a boy.
- ● d. Birds fly in the sky.

5. Which of these things could happen only in a made-up story?

- ○ a. It rains outside.
- ○ b. It stops raining.
- ○ c. A boy goes outside.
- ● d. A bug makes a rainbow.

Stop

FACT AND OPINION

Read this selection. Then read each question and fill in the circle next to the best answer.

Plant Food

All plants need a kind of salt to live. Some plants do not get all of this salt through their roots. So what do they do? They trap bugs and eat them to get the salt! I don't think bugs would be good to eat. But some plants do. The plants do not eat the way animals do.

The sundew plant has long leaves. They are covered with thin, sticky hairs. I think hairs look funny on a plant. The plant draws bugs to it by the way it looks and smells. When a bug sticks to a hair, the other hairs go over the bug. It can't get away! Slowly, the sundew plant eats the bug.

A flytrap plant also has hairy leaves. I think the flytrap is smarter than the sundew. A fly lands on the hairy leaves to look for food. Then the leaves come together and grab the fly. If you ask me, a fly must be very silly to land in a flytrap!

Flytrap plants are the kind I like to watch the most. I think all plants should know how to eat a fly or a bug.

Go on

1. Which sentence is an **opinion**?

  ○ a. All plants need a kind of salt to live.
  ○ b. Some plants do not get all of this salt through their roots.
  ○ c. They trap bugs and eat them to get the salt!
  ● d. I don't think bugs would be good to eat.

2. How can you tell this sentence is a **fact** and not an opinion?

  The plants do not eat the way animals do.

  ○ a. It's what someone feels.
  ● b. Someone could give you proof that it is true.
  ○ c. It is made up of words.
  ○ d. There is no way to tell.

3. Which sentence is an **opinion**?

  ○ a. The sundew plant has long leaves.
  ○ b. They are covered with thin, sticky hairs.
  ● c. I think hairs look funny on a plant.
  ○ d. The plant draws bugs to it by the way it looks and smells.

4. How do you know this sentence is an **opinion**?

Flytrap plants are the kind I like to watch the most.

- ○ a. It tells something about the plant.
- ○ b. Flytraps are not real.
- ● c. It tells what the writer feels about something.
- ○ d. Everyone thinks that.

5. Which sentence is a **fact**?

- ○ a. I think the flytrap is smarter than the sundew.
- ○ b. I think all plants should know how to eat a fly or a bug.
- ● c. Then the leaves come together and grab the fly.
- ○ d. If you ask me, a fly must be very silly to land in a flytrap!

Stop

BASE WORDS AND ENDINGS: -s, -es, -ed, -ing

Read each sentence and think about what word might go in the blank. Then fill in the circle next to the best answer.

1. The blue whale is the largest animal that has ever _____ .

- ○ a. lives
- ○ b. livees
- ● c. lived
- ○ d. living

2. Blue _____ can be longer than five big cars parked end to end.

- ● a. whales
- ○ b. whalees
- ○ c. whaled
- ○ d. whaling

3. They are even bigger than any of the _____ .

- ● a. dinosaurs
- ○ b. dinosaures
- ○ c. dinosaured
- ○ d. dinosauring

Go on

4. Many whales have been _____ by people.

- ○ a. kills
- ○ b. killes
- ● c. killed
- ○ d. killing

5. In many _____ , laws keep people from killing more whales.

- ○ a. placees
- ○ b. placing
- ○ c. placed
- ● d. places

VOWEL PAIRS: ow, ou

Read the selection. Look at the underlined words. Then read each question and fill in the circle next to the best answer.

There are many surprising kinds of fish. There are <u>brown</u> fish and blue fish. There are <u>round</u> fish and flat fish. The blowfish <u>blows</u> itself up like a balloon. Some small fish can even <u>glow</u> in the dark. It is fun to find <u>out</u> more about fish.

1. Which word has the same sound as the **ow** in **brown**?

   ○ a. grow
   ○ b. show
   ● c. now
   ○ d. slow

2. Which word has the same sound as the **ou** in **round**?

   ● a. sound
   ○ b. could
   ○ c. snow
   ○ d. pillow

3. Which word has the same sound as the **ow** in **blows**?

   ○ a. cow
   ● b. know
   ○ c. group
   ○ d. howl

4. Which word has the same sound as the **ou** in **out**?

   ○ a. grown
   ○ b. should
   ● c. shout
   ○ d. you

5. Which word has the same sound as the **ow** in **glow**?

   ○ a. down
   ○ b. house
   ○ c. would
   ● d. show

SUFFIXES: -ful, -ness, -ous, -ly, -y
WORDS WITH aw, al

Read each sentence and think about the word that might go in the blank. Then fill in the circle next to the best answer.

1. All dogs like to be treated with _____ .

   ○ a. kindly
   ○ b. kindful
   ○ c. kindy
   ● d. kindness

2. Most dogs are very _____ .

   ○ a. friendful
   ○ b. friendness
   ● c. friendly
   ○ d. friendnous

3. Dogs can be very _____ to the people they live with.

   ● a. helpful
   ○ b. helpness
   ○ c. helpous
   ○ d. helply

4. People who cannot see let dogs show them where to _____ .

    ○ a. will

    ● b. walk

    ○ c. well

    ○ d. how

5. Dogs are some of the best animals on four _____ !

    ○ a. pick

    ○ b. pets

    ● c. paws

    ○ d. plows

Stop

G HIGH-FREQUENCY WORDS

Read each sentence and think about what word might go in the blank. Then fill in the circle next to the best answer.

1. A baby bird grows inside an _____ .

   ● a. egg
   ○ b. between
   ○ c. farm
   ○ d. wash

2. A bird will sit on the eggs so they don't get _____ .

   ○ a. seven
   ● b. cold
   ○ c. wish
   ○ d. year

3. After a while, the eggs _____ open.

   ○ a. later
   ○ b. small
   ● c. finally
   ○ d. end

Go on

4. The baby birds are in no _____ to get out on their own.

     ○ a. often

     ○ b. wash

     ○ c. guess

     ● d. hurry

5. They _____ the nest when they can fly.

     ○ a. notice

     ● b. leave

     ○ c. also

     ○ d. class

Stop

WRITING

Read each sentence. Find the word that can replace the underlined words and fill in the circle next to your answer.

1. <u>Taylor and Josh</u> loved to play softball. *(using words in place of nouns)*

   ○ a. He
   ○ b. She
   ○ c. It
   ● d. They

2. <u>Softball</u> was their favorite game. *(using words in place of nouns)*

   ○ a. He
   ○ b. She
   ○ c. They
   ● d. It

3. <u>Maria</u> could hit the ball very far. *(using words in place of nouns)*

   ○ a. He
   ● b. She
   ○ c. Them
   ○ d. They

4. <u>Josh</u> could run fast. *(using words in place of nouns)*

- ● a. He
- ○ b. Him
- ○ c. It
- ○ d. They

5. Which step is out of order? *(writing things in order)*

- ○ a. Taylor hit the ball very far.
- ● b. Taylor was safe.
- ○ c. He ran around the bases.
- ○ d. He made it to home plate.

Stop

SPELLING

Read the sentence with the missing word. Find the right way to spell the word. Fill in the circle next to your answer.

1. My dog Sam knows _____ to talk! *(the vowel sound in* cow*)*
   - ○ a. hou
   - ○ b. haw
   - ● c. how
   - ○ d. howe

2. Sam _____ he could go to school with me.
   (words that end with -s or -es)
   - ○ a. wishs
   - ● b. wishes
   - ○ c. wichs
   - ○ d. wiches

3. I can _____ a picture, but Sam cannot.
   (the vowel sound in ball*)*
   - ○ a. dar
   - ○ b. dral
   - ● c. draw
   - ○ d. drow

4. Sam would like to go on bus _____ ! *(words that end with -s or -es)*

○ a. tripps
○ b. tripes
○ c. trieps
● d. trips

5. He thinks he could drive my school bus with one _____ ! *(the vowel sound in ball)*

○ a. pow
○ b. pa
● c. paw
○ d. pawl

6. He wants to take children to their _____ . *(words that end with -s or -es)*

● a. classes
○ b. classus
○ c. clases
○ d. clasas

7. _____ the children want Sam to be their bus driver. *(the vowel sound in ball)*

○ a. Al
● b. All
○ c. Awl
○ d. Ahl

Go on ⇒

8. Sam would drive to school, and our teacher would throw a _____ for him. *(the vowel sound in ball)*

- ○ a. bal
- ○ b. bawl
- ● c. ball
- ○ d. bow

9. "I see you can drive a bus _____ ," she would say. *(the vowel sound in cow)*

- ○ a. nah
- ○ b. naw
- ○ c. nowl
- ● d. now

10. When school let _____ , Sam would drive the children home. *(the vowel sound in cow)*

- ○ a. owt
- ○ b. awt
- ● c. out
- ○ d. aot

GRAMMAR

Read each sentence and think about what word might go in the blank. Then fill in the circle next to the best answer.

1. In 1969 some men _____ a spaceship to the moon for the first time. *(irregular verbs)*

   ● a. took
   ○ b. taked
   ○ c. tooken
   ○ d. take

2. The men _____ know what they would find there. *(contractions)*

   ○ a. don't
   ● b. didn't
   ○ c. doesn't
   ○ d. dint

3. They _____ a great trip! *(irregular verbs)*

   ○ a. has
   ○ b. haved
   ● c. had
   ○ d. hased

4. Their trip _____ everyone take notice. *(irregular verbs)*

- ○ a. make
- ○ b. mad
- ● c. made
- ○ d. maked

5. I _____ wait until we can fly to Mars! *(contractions)*

- ○ a. don't
- ● b. can't
- ○ c. doesn't
- ○ d. didn't

Stop

STUDY SKILLS *(locating information)*

Read each question. Then fill in the circle next to the best answer.

1. Where would you look to find out what a word means?

   - ● a. a dictionary
   - ○ b. an encyclopedia
   - ○ c. a magazine
   - ○ d. a video

2. Which of these would you use to check facts about a state?

   - ○ a. a video
   - ○ b. a magazine
   - ● c. an encyclopedia
   - ○ d. a dictionary

3. Which of these would you use a video for?

   - ○ a. to find out how a word is spelled
   - ○ b. to find out the meaning of a word
   - ○ c. to read about a subject
   - ● d. to learn about a subject

Go on ⇒

4. Which encyclopedia volume would you look in to find out about Guatemala?

- ○ a. A–C
- ● b. D–G
- ○ c. H–K
- ○ d. L–O

5. Which sentence about dictionaries and encyclopedias is not true?

- ○ a. They both give information.
- ○ b. They both can be found in a library.
- ● c. They both are one volume.
- ○ d. They both have entries in ABC order.

TELL ME A TALE

LEVEL 2, THEME 6

Theme Skills Test Record

Student _____ Date _____

STUDENT RECORD FORM	Possible Score	Criterion Score	Student Score
Part A: Sequence	5	4	
Part B: Cause and Effect	5	4	
Part C: Inferences: Making Predictions	5	4	
Part D: Base Words and Endings: *-ed, -ing*	5	4	
Part E: Vowel Pairs: *oi, oy*	5	4	
Part F: Base Words and Endings: *-es, -ed, -er, -est*	5	4	
Part G: High-Frequency Words	5	4	
Part H: Writing	5	4	
Part I: Spelling	10	8	
Part J: Grammar	5	4	
TOTAL	55	44	
Total Student Score x 1.82 =			%

SEQUENCE

Read the story. Then read the questions that follow. Fill in the circle next to the best answer.

The Turtle and the Rabbit

Once upon a time there was a very quick rabbit. He thought he could run faster than anyone. Rabbit bragged to his friends about it all the time. One day Rabbit was trying to find someone to race. Turtle said, "I will race you." Everyone looked surprised.

Rabbit laughed and laughed. "You will race me?" he asked. "This will be the easiest race ever!"

Fox started the race. "One, two, three, go!" he yelled. Rabbit flew down the road. Soon he was far away. Turtle was still crawling over the starting line. All of Turtle's friends shook their heads sadly.

Later, Rabbit looked around. Turtle was nowhere to be seen. So Rabbit sat down under a tree to take a little nap. Turtle kept walking as fast as he could, but that was not very fast. At last he saw Rabbit sleeping under the tree. Turtle smiled and kept walking.

Go on ⇨

When Rabbit woke up, it was getting dark. He rubbed his eyes. Then he jumped up. He had gone to sleep! Off he ran, as fast as he could.

Up ahead Rabbit could see the line at the end of the race. Then he saw Turtle. "Oh, no!" he thought. "Turtle is going to beat me!"

And that's just what happened. Turtle walked over the line right ahead of Rabbit. "Poor Rabbit. He will never brag about being fast again," said Turtle.

All the animals laughed. They were glad that Turtle was the winner.

1. What happens first in the story?
   ○ a. Fox starts the race.
   ● b. Rabbit tries to find someone to race him.
   ○ c. Rabbit goes to sleep under a tree.
   ○ d. Turtle says he will race Rabbit.

2. What happens before Rabbit runs down the road?
   ● a. Fox starts the race.
   ○ b. Turtle crawls over the line.
   ○ c. Rabbit goes to sleep.
   ○ d. Everyone cheers and laughs.

3. What happens after Rabbit wakes up?

- ○ a. He asks someone to race.
- ○ b. He starts the race.
- ● c. He rubs his eyes and jumps up.
- ○ d. He eats some grass.

4. What happens after Turtle crosses the finish line?

- ○ a. Turtle creeps over the starting line.
- ○ b. Rabbit goes to sleep.
- ○ c. Rabbit tries to get someone to race.
- ● d. Rabbit crosses the line at the end of the race.

5. What is the last thing that happens in the story?

- ○ a. Rabbit flies down the road.
- ○ b. Turtle says he will race Rabbit.
- ● c. All the animals laugh because Turtle beat Rabbit.
- ○ d. Rabbit sees Turtle at the finish line.

CAUSE AND EFFECT

Read the story. Then read the questions that follow. Fill in the circle next to the best answer.

Timbuk's Find

Timbuk lived long ago in a cold and snowy land. His father was Zantu, the leader of his people. One day Zantu said, "All our people will have to go away. There are no animals in the woods here. There will be no food when the wind blows colder."

Timbuk was sad. He had always lived in this place. It was his only home. Timbuk ran out onto the ice of the big lake. He fell down on the ice and cried. Slowly, the warm water from his eyes made a hole in the ice. Timbuk was surprised by a splashing sound. Fish were jumping through the hole out onto the ice! Soon there were enough fish to feed all the people. Timbuk dried his eyes. He ran to tell his father what had happened.

Zantu said, "One day you will be a great leader, Timbuk. You have found a way to feed our people. You have found a way to keep our home here. There was no food in the woods. But you found some in the lake."

Go on

1. Why does Zantu have to move the people?

   ○ a. He wants to go see some friends.

   ● b. He needs to go where there is food.

   ○ c. He thinks going new places is fun.

   ○ d. The people do not like their village.

2. Why is Timbuk sad?

   ○ a. He does not like to eat fish.

   ○ b. He thinks going away will be hard work.

   ○ c. He has lived in too many other places.

   ● d. He does not want to leave his home.

3. What happens when Timbuk cries?

   ○ a. His friends laugh at him.

   ○ b. His father asks him if he is all right.

   ● c. Water from his eyes makes a hole in the ice.

   ○ d. He cries until he falls asleep.

Go on

4. What surprised Timbuk?

- ● a. Fish had jumped out through the hole.
- ○ b. There were pretty rocks by the lake.
- ○ c. He found a way to a new land.
- ○ d. He had found a missing toy.

5. Why did Zantu think Timbuk would become a great leader?

- ○ a. He was very tall.
- ● b. He had found food for all his people.
- ○ c. He was never mean to the other children.
- ○ d. He stopped crying when he was told to.

INFERENCES: MAKING PREDICTIONS

Read each story. Then read the question that follows. Fill in the circle next to the best answer.

Once there was a boy with no boots. When he was walking in the woods, he found an animal skin. As he was walking home, he stopped to rest by a lake. An old man was also resting there. The boy showed the man what he had found. The old man said that he could make boots from animal skin.

1. What do you think will happen next?

   ◯ a. The boot maker will go home.

   ◯ b. The boy will go play in the lake.

   ⬤ c. The boot maker will make boots for the boy.

   ◯ d. The boy will find some new boots.

Once there was a very kind man. He lived alone in the hills in a little hut. One day he made a pot of warm stew.

Two cold, thin children followed their sheep deep into the hills. As night fell, they walked toward the light that came from the man's hut.

2. What do you think will happen next?

- ○ a. The children will keep walking deeper into the hills.
- ● b. The man will give the children some stew and a place to stay.
- ○ c. The man will put out his light and hide from the children.
- ○ d. The sheep will fall into a lake.

Everyone was afraid of the mean, wild giant. One day the giant came walking into town. People ran and hid. Tim was hiding under a bush. He saw the giant walk by. There was a big thorn in the giant's foot. Tim reached his hand out. He pulled the thorn from the giant's foot.

3. What do you think will happen next?

- ○ a. The giant will become even meaner.
- ● b. The giant will feel better and thank Tim.
- ○ c. Tim will thank the giant.
- ○ d. Everyone will run away from Tim.

There was a sweet grandmother who lived in the woods. She wanted friends, but no one lived near her. Every day she baked cookies. She ate one or two. She gave the rest to the birds and animals.

One day a brother and sister took a walk in the woods. They could not find their way home. Then they smelled something wonderful cooking. They ran toward the smell.

4. What do you think will happen next?

- ● a. The children will find the grandmother's house.
- ○ b. The grandmother's cookies will start to smell bad.
- ○ c. The children will find their way out of the woods.
- ○ d. The grandmother will go live in town.

Go on

A young girl was walking home. She found a small bag of gold coins on the path. She was so happy! She put the bag in her pocket. She forgot about the hole in her pocket. Then she ran home as fast as she could.

5. What do you think will happen next?

- ○ a. She will find another bag of coins.
- ○ b. She will stop and take a long rest.
- ○ c. She will not find the right way home.
- ● d. The bag will fall out of the hole in her pocket.

BASE WORDS AND ENDINGS: -ed, -ing

Read the sentences. Think about what word might go in the blank. Fill in the circle next to your answer.

1. A girl was _____ happily back home.

- ● a. skating
- ○ b. skateing
- ○ c. skateed
- ○ d. skated

2. She was _____ a shiny new coin in her hand.

- ● a. holding
- ○ b. holded
- ○ c. holdding
- ○ d. hold

3. But somehow she _____ her coin.

- ○ a. droped
- ○ b. droping
- ● c. dropped
- ○ d. dropping

Go on ⇨

4. She looked for the coin for hours. She was
_____ she would find it.

- ● a. hoping
- ○ b. hopping
- ○ c. hopeing
- ○ d. hoped

5. Finally she found her coin and _____ home
to put it in her bank.

- ○ a. racing
- ○ b. raceing
- ● c. raced
- ○ d. raceed

VOWEL PAIRS *(oi, oy)*

Read the story. Look at the underlined words. Then read each question. Fill in the circle next to your answer.

"What is that <u>noise</u>?" asked Tomás.

Scott said, "That's my new <u>toy</u>. It is a bank. Each time you put something in, it makes a different sound. Sometimes it sounds like a car, and sometimes it sounds like thunder."

"Oh <u>boy</u>!" said Tomás. "May I put in a <u>coin</u>?"

"Sure," said Scott. "Put in all the coins you want. That's the part that is a real <u>joy</u>!"

1. Which word has the same vowel sound you hear in the word **noise**?

   ● a. boil
   ○ b. name
   ○ c. bake
   ○ d. sound

2. Which word has the same vowel sound you hear in the word **toy**?

   ○ a. top
   ● b. soil
   ○ c. tray
   ○ d. sand

3. Which word has the same vowel sound you hear in the word **boy**?

- ○ a. chance
- ● b. oil
- ○ c. chose
- ○ d. jump

4. Which word has the same vowel sound you hear in the word **coin**?

- ● a. join
- ○ b. jam
- ○ c. corn
- ○ d. cart

5. Which word has the same vowel sound you hear in the word **joy**?

- ○ a. job
- ○ b. jump
- ○ c. broke
- ● d. spoil

Stop

F

BASE WORDS AND ENDINGS: -es, -ed, -er, -est

Read the sentences. Think about what word might go in the blank. Fill in the circle next to your answer.

1. Jack was the fastest of all the _____ in the West.

   ○ a. bunnys
   ○ b. bunnes
   ○ c. bunnis
   ● d. bunnies

2. One day the wind _____ to get Jack to race him. Jack finally said yes.

   ○ a. trys
   ● b. tried
   ○ c. tryed
   ○ d. tryer

3. The faster they ran, the _____ the wind grew.

   ● a. noisier
   ○ b. noiser
   ○ c. noisyer
   ○ d. noises

Go on ⇨

4. No matter how much the wind _____ , he was no match for Jack.

- ○ a. hurryed
- ○ b. hurrier
- ○ c. hurryied
- ● d. hurried

5. As Jack left the wind far behind, he shouted, "I am the _____ bunny in the land, for I am faster than the wind!"

- ○ a. happyer
- ○ b. happyest
- ● c. happiest
- ○ d. happied

G

HIGH-FREQUENCY WORDS

Read the following sentences. Think about what word might go in the blank. Then fill in the circle next to your answer.

1. Once long _____ , there was a very pretty island far, far away.

   ○ a. cloud
   ○ b. earth
   ● c. ago
   ○ d. slowly

2. It was _____ from any place you have ever been.

   ○ a. those
   ● b. different
   ○ c. shall
   ○ d. heavy

3. Anything could _____ on this island.

   ● a. happen
   ○ b. enough
   ○ c. poor
   ○ d. stood

Go on

4. A strange _____ animal who laughed all the
time lived there.

- ○ a. rained
- ○ b. pull
- ● c. wild
- ○ d. quickly

5. He could _____ you into a tiny little
mouse or a great big giant!

- ○ a. excited
- ○ b. person
- ○ c. those
- ● d. change

H WRITING

These sentences should tell about the picture in order, from top to bottom. Read the sentences and find the one that is not in order. Fill in the circle next to your answer. *(describing in order)*

1. **Which sentence in this description is out of order?**

   ○ a. The top of the hill is covered with snow.

   ○ b. There are many big rocks on the hill below the snow line.

   ● c. A small stream flows from the trees at the bottom of the hill.

   ○ d. Below the rocks, there are tall trees growing.

Read each question. Fill in the circle next to the best answer.

2. Which one of these sentences tells the **most?** *(writing clearly with adjectives)*

   ○ a. The water flows over stones.

   ○ b. The water flows over round stones.

   ● c. The clean water flows over round, shiny stones.

   ○ d. The clean water flows over stones.

3. Which sentence **compares** two things? *(writing comparisons)*

   ● a. The water in the lake was warmer than the stream water.

   ○ b. Everyone liked being in the warm water of the lake.

   ○ c. Even in the fall, the lake water stayed warm.

   ○ d. People came and stayed along the shore of the lake.

4. Which one of these sentences tells the most? *(writing clearly with adjectives)*

- ○ a. The man closed the door.
- ● b. The jumpy little man closed the heavy green door.
- ○ c. The jumpy man closed the door.
- ○ d. The man closed the heavy door.

5. Which one of these sentences compares three things? *(writing comparisons)*

- ○ a. The dog was louder than the cat.
- ● b. Of the dog, the cat, and the bird, the dog was the loudest.
- ○ c. The cat was quieter than the bird.
- ○ d. The bird was loud.

SPELLING

Read the following sentences. Find the right way to spell the word that goes in the blank. Fill in the circle next to your answer.

1. The snake _____ by to see the cowboy.
   (double final consonant before -ed)
   ○ a. stoped
   ● b. stopped
   ○ c. stopt
   ○ d. stahped

2. The cowboy was _____ set to eat some soup.
   (double final consonant before -ing)
   ● a. getting
   ○ b. geting
   ○ c. gitting
   ○ d. geteing

3. The pot had begun to _____ .
   (vowel sound in boy*)*
   ○ a. bayl
   ○ b. boul
   ● c. boil
   ○ d. bole

4. The cowboy asked the snake to _____ him for some soup. *(vowel sound in boy)*

- ○ a. joen
- ○ b. jon
- ○ c. joyn
- ● d. join

5. The sunlight _____ slowly from the sky. *(drop final e before -ed)*

- ○ a. fadedd
- ○ b. fadeed
- ● c. faded
- ○ d. fadded

6. The cowboy _____ a bowl of soup in front of the snake. *(drop final e before -ed)*

- ● a. placed
- ○ b. plased
- ○ c. placeed
- ○ d. plast

7. The snake smacked his lips with _____. *(vowel sound in boy)*

- ○ a. joi
- ● b. joy
- ○ c. joie
- ○ d. joye

Go on ⟹

8. Soon another cowboy came _____ up.
(drop final e before -ing)

○ a. wriding
○ b. rideing
● c. riding
○ d. rihting

9. He was surprised that the first cowboy had _____ his soup with a snake.
(drop final e before -ed)

○ a. sharred
● b. shared
○ c. shered
○ d. sahred

10. But he _____ up to the campfire, and he asked if he could have some too.
(double final consonant before -ed)

● a. stepped
○ b. steped
○ c. steeped
○ d. sepped

Stop

GRAMMAR

Read the question. Fill in the circle next to your answer.

1. Which sentence has an adjective that tells how many? *(adjectives)*

   ○ a. The small boy went to the goat pen.
   ○ b. He looked for his goats.
   ● c. He could find only seven goats.
   ○ d. Where could the others be?

2. Which sentence has an adjective that tells what kind? *(adjectives)*

   ○ a. The boy looked around the farm.
   ○ b. Then he looked around the woods.
   ○ c. Finally he found his goats.
   ● d. They were drinking clean, cold water from the stream.

Go on ⇨

Read each sentence. Think about what word makes sense in the blank. Fill in the circle next to your answer.

3. The big goats were _____ than the small goats. *(comparing with adjectives)*

   ○ a. fast
   ● b. faster
   ○ c. fastest
   ○ d. slow

4. The boy carried the _____ goat of all. *(comparing with adjectives)*

   ○ a. small
   ● b. smallest
   ○ c. smaller
   ○ d. big

5. Then he made the walls around his goat pen much _____ . *(comparing with adjectives)*

   ● a. taller
   ○ b. tallest
   ○ c. tall
   ○ d. untall